Contents

B2 Topic 1: The Building Blocks of Cells

This topic looks at:

- the differences between plant, animal and bacterial cells
- how DNA makes up genes, chromosomes and genomes and is the template for protein synthesis
- what stem cells, cloning, genetic engineering and the Human Genome Project are
- how cells divide by mitosis and meiosis
- how enzymes work

Light and Electron Microscopes

The first **light microscopes** were made in the early 17th century. For the first time they allowed scientists to see small, single-celled organisms and the cells that made up larger life. Light microscopes use glass lenses to refract light and produce a magnified image. To calculate the magnification of a light microscope, multiply the magnification of the eye piece lens by the objective lens. **Electron microscopes** were invented in the 1930s. Instead of using light, they shine a beam of electrons through a sample. The wavelength of electrons is much smaller than the wavelength of light. This means that a much greater magnification and detail can be seen.

Comparing Plant and Animal Cells

All living organisms are made up of cells. The structures of different types of cells are related to their functions.

Feature	Plant Cells	Animal Cells
Nucleus	Yes	Yes
Cytoplasm	Yes	Yes
Cell Membrane	Yes	Yes
Mitochondria	Yes	Yes
Cellulose Cell Wall	Yes	No
Large Vacuole	Almost always	No
Chloroplasts (containing chlorophyll)	Those that are exposed to light	No

To learn the functions of these cell components, look them up in the glossary (pages 98-102).

Bacterial Cells

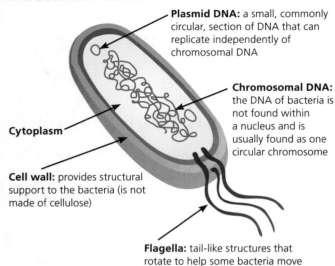

Plasmid DNA: a small, commonly circular, section of DNA that can replicate independently of chromosomal DNA

Chromosomal DNA: the DNA of bacteria is not found within a nucleus and is usually found as one circular chromosome

Cytoplasm

Cell wall: provides structural support to the bacteria (is not made of cellulose)

Flagella: tail-like structures that rotate to help some bacteria move

DNA, Genes and Chromosomes

In normal human cells there are 23 pairs of **chromosomes**. Chromosomes consist of long, coiled molecules of **DNA** (deoxyribonucleic acid).

A gene is a section of DNA, which codes for a particular protein (see page 10).

A DNA molecule consists of two strands, which are coiled to form a **double helix**. The strands are linked by a series of paired **complementary bases**: adenine (A), cytosine (C), guanine (G) and thymine (T).

- Adenine is only ever linked to thymine: A–T.
- Cytosine is only ever linked to guanine: C–G.

The bases are held together by weak hydrogen bonds.

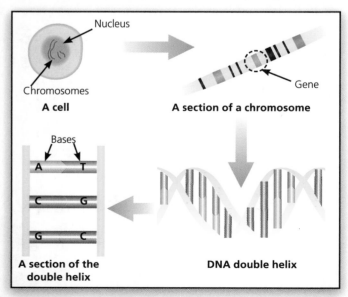

Nucleus

Chromosomes

A cell

Gene

A section of a chromosome

Bases

A   T

C   G

G   C

A section of the double helix

DNA double helix

Nick Dixon, Susan Loxley and Paul Levy

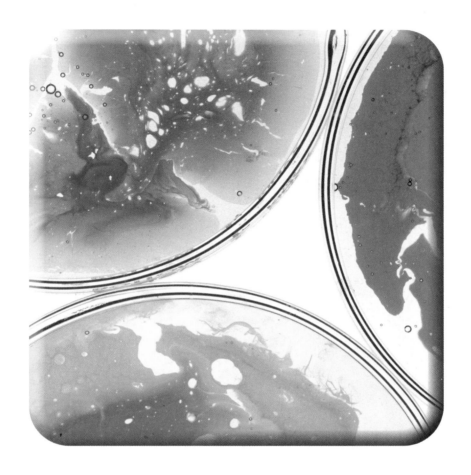

REVISION PLUS

Edexcel

GCSE Additional Science

Revision and Classroom Companion

Extraction of DNA from Plant Cells

The method for extracting DNA from plant cells is:

1. Dissolve 3g of salt in 90cm^3 of distilled water in a beaker and mix in 10cm^3 of washing up liquid.
2. Mash 50g of defrosted frozen peas in a second beaker with a little water and add 10cm^3 of the solution to the first beaker.
3. Place in a water bath at 60°C for 15 minutes and stir gently.
4. Place in an ice bath for 5 minutes and stir gently.
5. Very carefully pour chilled ethanol solution onto the top of the beaker and leave for a few minutes.
6. The DNA will separate out into pale strands at the boundary between the pea extract and the ethanol.

HT The Human Genome Project

In 1977, biochemist Fred Sanger discovered a way of identifying the sequence of bases in DNA.

A **genome** is all the genetic material in an organism. The **Human Genome Project** (HGP), completed in 2003, used Sanger's method to identify the sequence of bases in every gene that appears on human chromosomes – that is millions of base pairs! To do this hundreds of scientists in universities and research centres all over the world worked together for 13 years.

Knowing where a gene appears on a chromosome and how it is made up could be very useful. For example, doctors could identify and replace 'faulty' genes, which cause genetic disorders; forensic scientists could use the information to compare DNA samples from potential suspects with those found at a crime scene, and convict or clear them of the crime.

But the question still remains: should scientists have done this work? There are concerns that the information could be misused and concerns over who will have access to the information.

The Discovery of the Structure of DNA

In 1953 at Cambridge University, scientists **James Watson** and **Francis Crick** discovered the double helix model of DNA. Several years before this, **Rosalind Franklin** worked with **Maurice Wilkins** at King's College, London to take an X-ray diffraction image of DNA. Watson and Crick used this to come up with their model. Watson, Crick and Wilkins received the Nobel Prize, shortly after Franklin died, in 1962. At this time, the Nobel Prize could only be awarded to the living, so Franklin did not receive it.

Genetic Engineering

Genetic engineering involves removing a gene from one organism and inserting it into another. Genes can be inserted into animals, plants and microorganisms. If genes from one species are inserted into animals of a different species they are then called **transgenic** animals as they have been genetically modified (GM). For example, transgenic cows have been created to produce 'designer milk', which contains:

- extra protein (milk protein is known as casein)
- low levels of cholesterol
- human antibodies (normally produced by our white blood cells).

So transgenic animals, like these cows, have enormous potential. They could be 'designed' to produce all sorts of things that humans need for good health and development.

Genes can also be inserted into plants. **Rice** has been genetically modified to contain a **beta-carotene gene** to reduce Vitamin A deficiency in humans. In the countries where Vitamin A deficiency occurs most frequently (Africa and South East Asia) rice is often a staple food. Vitamin A deficiency leads to blindness in children.

The human gene for insulin has been inserted into bacteria, which are then used to produce the hormone on a large scale to help treat diabetics.

Breeding Herbicide-Resistant Crops

Another well-known example of inserting genes into plants is in the production of herbicide-resistant crops.

Herbicides are used to kill weeds, which prevent crop plants from growing. However, the herbicide may also kill some of the crop. Therefore, breeding herbicide-resistant crops enables people to produce more food.

This is how it is done:

1. Scientists find a naturally occurring plant that is resistant to the herbicide.
2. Scientists identify the gene that is responsible for the resistance.
3. A **vector**, such as the bacterium *Agrobacterium tumefaciens* is used to transfer the gene coding for herbicide resistance to the embryo crop plant's DNA.
4. The crop plants are allowed to grow and are then treated with the herbicide to kill weeds.
5. The new plants are resistant to the herbicide and are not killed.

Wild plant has a gene resistant to herbicide.

Resistant gene transferred to crop plant's DNA by vector bacterium *Agrobacterium tumefaciens*.

GM crop plant resistant to herbicide.

More food produced because crop plants do not have to compete with weeds for resources.

Sexual Reproduction

During **fertilisation**, **haploid gametes** (i.e. a **sperm** cell from the father and **egg** or **ovum** cell from the mother) fuse together to form a **diploid zygote**. This will replicate and divide to form an organism that has half its genes from each parent. This means that the offspring will inherit characteristics from both parents, leading to genetic **variation** (differences between individuals). Each individual has a unique genotype (genetic make-up). The expression of these genes is called the phenotype.

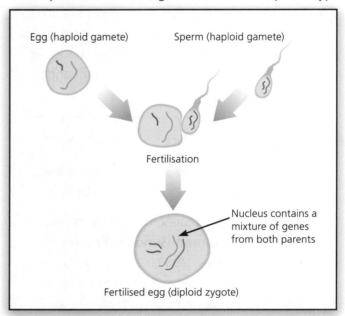

Egg (haploid gamete)   Sperm (haploid gamete)

Fertilisation

Nucleus contains a mixture of genes from both parents

Fertilised egg (diploid zygote)

Asexual Reproduction

The offspring produced by **asexual reproduction** get their genes from one parent only. So they have exactly the same genes as the parent. This makes them **clones** (see page 8).

It is possible for plants to reproduce asexually (i.e. without flowers or fertilisation). For example, the *Chlorophytum* (spider plant) throws off **runners:**

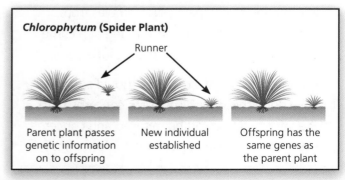

Chlorophytum (Spider Plant)

Runner

Parent plant passes genetic information on to offspring

New individual established

Offspring has the same genes as the parent plant

Mitosis

Mitosis is the division of a cell nucleus to produce two cell nuclei with **genetically identical** sets of chromosomes. This happens to produce new cells for growth, to repair damaged tissues and in asexual reproduction (see page 6). The diagram opposite shows this process:

1. Diploid cell with two pairs of chromosomes.
2. Each chromosome replicates itself.
3. The copies separate. Cell now divides.
4. Each new **diploid daughter cell** has the same number of chromosomes as the original cell and contains the same genes as the original cell.

Meiosis

In **meiosis**, a **diploid cell** divides twice to produce four **haploid daughter cells** that contain half the number of chromosomes (see diagram opposite). A diploid cell contains two sets of chromosomes. A haploid cell contains only one set of chromosomes.

This process produces cells with **genetically different** sets of chromosomes and happens in sexually reproducing organisms to produce **gametes** (sex cells, i.e. sperm and eggs).

Comparing Mitosis and Meiosis

	Mitosis	Meiosis
Where it happens	In most parts of the body.	In the ovaries and testes.
Number of cells made	Two cells.	Four cells.
Genetic variation	All cells are genetically identical.	All cells are genetically different.
Number of chromosomes in the nucleus	Two sets of chromosomes – diploid.	One set of chromosomes – haploid.
Purpose	Growth and cell replacement.	Production of gametes.

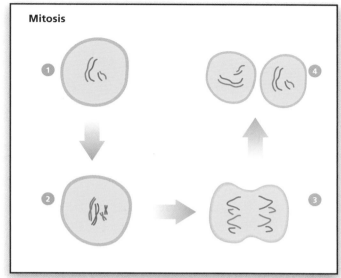

Mitosis

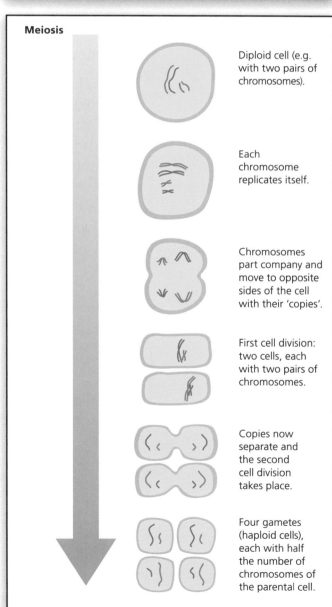

Meiosis

Diploid cell (e.g. with two pairs of chromosomes).

Each chromosome replicates itself.

Chromosomes part company and move to opposite sides of the cell with their 'copies'.

First cell division: two cells, each with two pairs of chromosomes.

Copies now separate and the second cell division takes place.

Four gametes (haploid cells), each with half the number of chromosomes of the parental cell.

Clones and the Ethics of Cloning

Clones are individuals that are genetically identical. Identical twins are natural clones as they have exactly the same genes.

It is possible to make clones artificially. In 1996, **Dolly the sheep** was the first cloned mammal. Since then, lots of mammals have been produced by cloning techniques, including dogs and cats.

It is also possible, using tissue culture techniques, to clone tissues and organs for transplant surgery.

However, scientists, as well as the general public, have social and ethical concerns with cloning mammals and human body parts.

Some people think that cloning is the inevitable result of scientific progress and we should be allowed to benefit from it. However, others believe that we should not tamper with nature. Some concerns about cloning include:
- the fear of creating the 'perfect race'
- the possibilities of abnormalities occurring in clones
- clones will not have 'parents'
- cloning does not allow 'natural' evolution.

Cloning Mammals

It is possible to clone mammals by the process shown in the diagram.

In 1996, at the Roslin Institute, near Edinburgh, Dolly the sheep was cloned using this technique. Scientists believe that one possible danger of cloning in this way is premature ageing. Sheep normally live to 16 years of age. However, Dolly had to be put down when she was six because she was suffering from arthritis and lung disease – conditions normally associated with older sheep.

Because the egg cell receives genetic information from just one parent (rather than receiving copies of genes from two parents), defects in the DNA are more likely to affect the overall organisation of cells and tissues during the development of cloned embryos and, therefore, lead to abnormalities (e.g. in brain structure).

Scientific evidence suggests that there are risks associated with the later stages of embryonic development of clones. Many embryos do not even survive until birth. The Roslin Institute scientists tried 276 times before they were successful with Dolly.

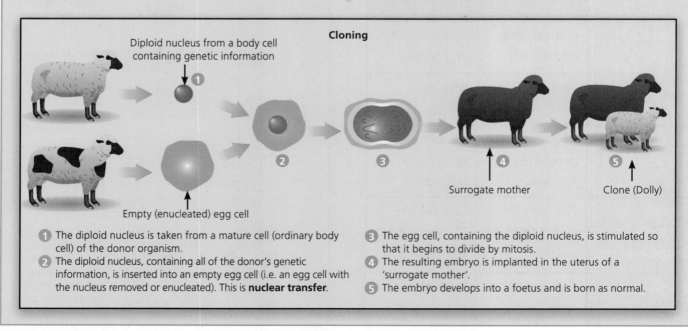

Cloning

Diploid nucleus from a body cell containing genetic information

Empty (enucleated) egg cell

Surrogate mother

Clone (Dolly)

1. The diploid nucleus is taken from a mature cell (ordinary body cell) of the donor organism.
2. The diploid nucleus, containing all of the donor's genetic information, is inserted into an empty egg cell (i.e. an egg cell with the nucleus removed or enucleated). This is **nuclear transfer**.
3. The egg cell, containing the diploid nucleus, is stimulated so that it begins to divide by mitosis.
4. The resulting embryo is implanted in the uterus of a 'surrogate mother'.
5. The embryo develops into a foetus and is born as normal.

Stem Cells

Most cells are specialised to allow them to perform a particular job efficiently. The process by which they become specialised is called **differentiation**.

Plant cells can differentiate at any time, whereas animal cells only tend to differentiate soon after they are made. Animal stem cells can differentiate into all other types of cells. However, they lose the ability to differentiate as the animal matures.

Stem cells are undifferentiated (i.e. unspecialised). This means that they could, theoretically, differentiate into any type of cell. Research has been carried out, which shows that stem cells could potentially be used to replace damaged cells and tissues to help in the treatment of diseases or injuries.

When different chemicals, called **growth factors**, are added to stem cells, they are made to develop into:

- insulin-producing cells in the pancreas (islet cells)
- heart muscle cells
- blood cells
- neurones (nerve cells)
- bone marrow cells.

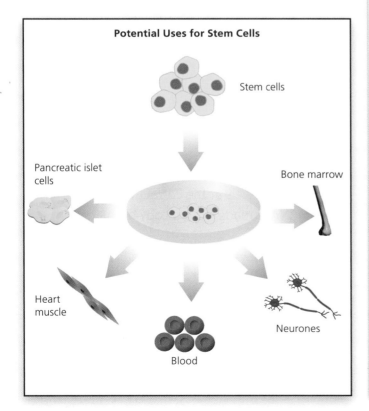

Potential Uses for Stem Cells

Stem cells

Pancreatic islet cells

Bone marrow

Heart muscle

Neurones

Blood

Stem Cells and Parkinson's Disease

When the neurones in the brain stop producing **dopamine**, a person develops **Parkinson's disease**. Dopamine is a chemical that the neurones use to communicate with each other. When dopamine is not produced, the brain is unable to coordinate the movements of the body (amongst other things).

If stem cells could be made into brain neurones and made to produce dopamine, this could potentially provide a cure for Parkinson's disease.

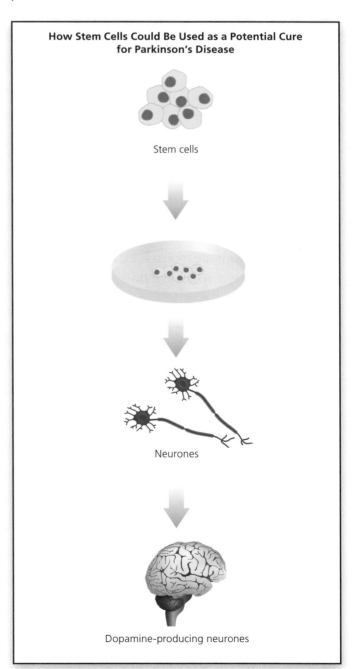

How Stem Cells Could Be Used as a Potential Cure for Parkinson's Disease

Stem cells

Neurones

Dopamine-producing neurones

Stem Cell Research

Stem cells can come from **bone marrow** and/or from **embryos**. When stem cells come from embryos, they are called **embryonic stem cells**. A lot of controversy surrounds embryonic stem cell research as some people think that an embryo is an individual life and disagree with its use. Other people agree with the research and think it might lead to cures for conditions such as Parkinson's disease (see page 9) or spinal injuries.

DNA and Protein Synthesis

DNA contains the instructions for how the cells will join **amino acids** together in order to make specific **proteins**. The instructions are in the form of a code, made up of the four DNA bases (adenine, thymine, cytosine and guanine). The sequence of bases represents the order in which a cell should assemble amino acids to make a protein.

There are about 20 amino acids in total, which can be arranged in different numbers, orders and combinations to produce different proteins. These combinations lead to proteins having different sizes and shapes. Proteins are molecules that the body requires to make enzymes, hormones, skin and hair, etc., and for growth and repair.

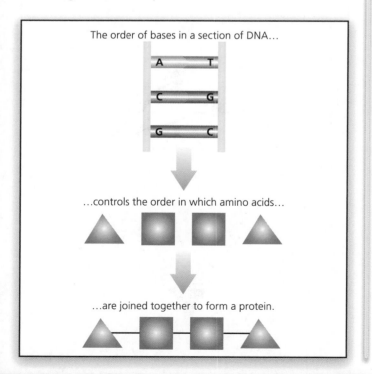

The order of bases in a section of DNA…

…controls the order in which amino acids…

…are joined together to form a protein.

HT Protein Synthesis in Detail

Organelles are specialised structures found in the cytoplasm of cells. Organelles called **ribosomes** are involved in **protein synthesis**.

The information needed to make a protein is stored in the DNA of a gene. The bases in DNA occur as **triplets** (e.g. ACG or TAC). These are called **codons**. Each codon codes for a single amino acid in a protein. This code is stored in the **coding strand** of DNA and is copied to produce a molecule of complementary **messenger RNA** (mRNA). This is **transcription**. RNA is similar to DNA but, unlike DNA, it only has one strand and it can move outside the nucleus of the cell into the cytoplasm. The RNA contains the code for linking the amino acids; the ribosomes interpret this code to link the amino acids and form a **polypeptide** (protein). This process is called **translation**.

DNA in nucleus of cell	RNA	Ribosomes	Polypeptide (protein) in cytoplasm

A Cell

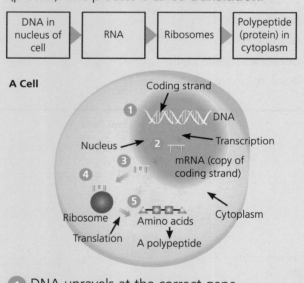

1. DNA unravels at the correct gene.
2. mRNA is made from a copy of the coding strand.
3. mRNA moves from the nucleus to the cytoplasm where it attaches to a ribosome.
4. The triplet code is interpreted by the ribosomes.
5. Amino acids are brought to the ribosome by **transfer RNA** (tRNA) and joined in sequence to make a polypeptide (protein).

DNA Mutations

A **DNA mutation** is a change to the sequence of the bases that make up a gene. Mutations can occur from:

• UV radiation

• viruses

• some chemicals

• errors during DNA replication (see page 7).

In genetics, scientists do not think of all mutations as being harmful. Some have no effect at all, whilst others alter the DNA of an organism for the better. If a mutation gives an individual an advantage, then, according to Darwin's theory of evolution by natural selection, this individual is more likely to reproduce and pass on the mutation to future generations.

Enzymes

Enzymes are **biological catalysts**. They are protein molecules, which control the rate of chemical reactions that occur in living organisms. Enzymes are found in many parts of the body. They act on substances called **substrates**, for which they are highly **specific**.

Enzymes called DNA polymerases are used in DNA replication (see page 7). They copy an existing strand of DNA by adding new bases. Enzymes are also used in protein synthesis to unzip the DNA at the start of transcription (see page 10). Different types of enzymes are also found in the digestive system (see page 25).

Lock and Key Hypothesis

The **lock and key hypothesis** is a simple way of explaining how an enzyme works. In this model, the enzyme is the lock and the substrate is the key. They fit together very specifically, like a lock and key. This means that enzymes are highly specific for their substrates (they are unlikely to work on other substances).

Enzymes are protein molecules with high specificity that have been assembled into particular shapes, allowing the following to take place:

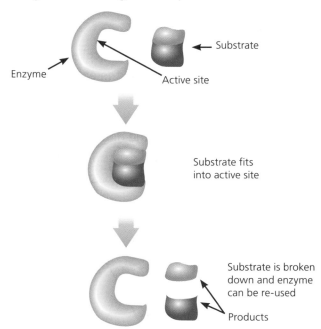

Enzyme / Substrate / Active site

Substrate fits into active site

Substrate is broken down and enzyme can be re-used / Products

Enzymes can also be used to make larger molecules from smaller ones.

Denaturing Enzymes

When enzymes are exposed to high temperatures or extreme pH they become **denatured**. This means they are irreversibly damaged and will no longer function.

Denaturing of enzymes can be explained using the lock and key hypothesis. When an enzyme is denatured the **active site** (the part of the enzyme that the substrate fits into) changes shape. If this happens the substrate no longer fits into the enzyme (the key no longer fits the lock). This means the substrate cannot be broken down.

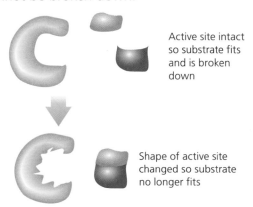

Active site intact so substrate fits and is broken down

Shape of active site changed so substrate no longer fits

Factors that Affect Enzyme Action

Enzymes work best under certain conditions of **temperature** and **pH**.

Effect of Temperature

As the temperature rises, increased collisions between reactants and enzymes increase the enzyme action up to the optimum temperature. After this, an increase in temperature continues to cause increased collisions but the enzyme molecules become denatured by the heat, resulting in decreased enzyme action or none at all.

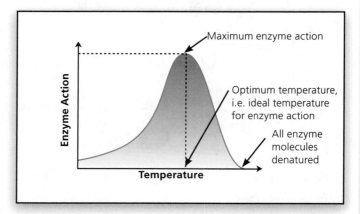

Effect of pH

There is an optimum pH at which the enzyme works best. As the pH increases or decreases about this point the enzyme becomes less effective.

The optimum pH of different enzymes can vary considerably:

- The enzyme, amylase, in human saliva, works best at a pH of about 7.
- The enzyme, protease, which is in our stomach, needs to be in very acidic conditions to work well.

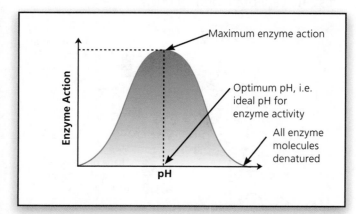

Enzymes also work best in situations where they have the highest concentrations of their substrate. This is the substance that they act upon.

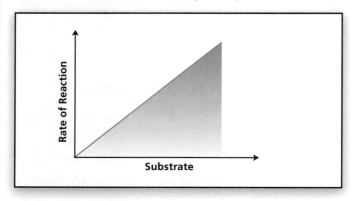

Investigating the Effect of Temperature and pH on Enzyme Action

The effect of temperature on enzyme action can be investigated by measuring the length of time that lipase (an enzyme that breaks down fat) takes to break down the fat in milk at various temperatures. This process reduces the pH of the milk from about 10 to below 8.3, and so the indicator **phenolphthalein** can be used. The time taken for the pink solution to turn colourless indicates how quickly the enzymes have worked at various temperatures.

The effect of pH on enzyme action can be determined by measuring the length of time that **amylase** takes to break down starch into glucose at various pHs.

1. Use buffers to change the pH of starch solutions.
2. Add amylase to the starch solutions and begin timing.
3. At 10 second intervals, remove a small volume of liquid and test the solutions using iodine.
4. When the iodine no longer turns black, amylase will have broken down all starch.
5. Record the time taken for the starch to disappear completely. The length of time taken indicates how quickly the enzymes have worked at various pHs.

B2 Topic 2: Organisms and Energy

This topic looks at:
- the differences between aerobic and anaerobic respiration
- the relationship between exercise, breathing rate and heart rate
- photosynthesis and water movement in plants
- the relationship between organisms and their environment

Respiration

All living organisms need energy. They use the process of respiration to release the energy in organic molecules (food). Respiration can be **aerobic** or **anaerobic**.

Aerobic Respiration

In aerobic respiration, blood transports **oxygen** and food, in the form of **glucose**, to the body's cells. Special enzymes in the cells cause the glucose and oxygen to react, and energy is released. The energy can then be used for life processes, e.g. movement.

Glucose, oxygen and carbon dioxide move between the capillaries (see page 24) and the respiring cells by **diffusion** (i.e. from an area of high concentration to one of lower concentration) down a concentration gradient. Glucose and oxygen diffuse from the capillaries into respiring cells; carbon dioxide and water diffuse from respiring cells into the capillaries.

Aerobic respiration is a very efficient method of producing energy: one molecule of glucose respired aerobically can provide about 20 times as much energy as anaerobic respiration (see page 14).

Ventilation (breathing in and out) provides the oxygen needed for aerobic respiration.

Increased Diffusion

When muscle cells are working hard (contracting and relaxing a lot), their **respiration rates** increase because more energy is being used up. This means that more oxygen needs to be absorbed and more carbon dioxide needs to be removed. This **gas exchange** takes place by **diffusion** in the lungs, at an increased rate.

Diffusion between a Capillary and a Working Muscle Cell

The Respiration Equation

Glucose	+	Oxygen	→	Energy Carbon dioxide	+	Water
$C_6H_{12}O_6$	+	$6O_2$	→	Energy $6CO_2$	+	$6H_2O$

- **Glucose** and **oxygen** are brought to the respiring cells by the bloodstream.
- **Carbon dioxide** is taken away by the blood to the lungs, where it is breathed out.
- **Water** passes into the blood and is lost as sweat, moist breath and urine.
- **Energy** is used for life processes.

The Effects of Exercise

When you **exercise** (i.e. when you increase your physical activity), your **breathing rate increases** so that larger quantities of oxygen enter the body and larger quantities of carbon dioxide are removed. Your **heart rate** also increases to pump these substances more quickly around your body.

The amount of blood (cardiac output) pumped from your heart can be calculated using the equation:

Cardiac Output = Stroke Volume × Heart Rate

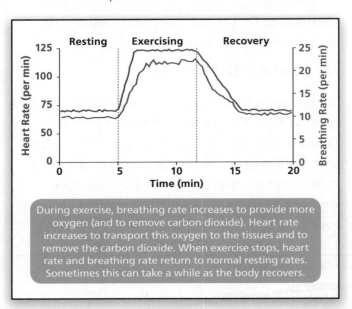

During exercise, breathing rate increases to provide more oxygen (and to remove carbon dioxide). Heart rate increases to transport this oxygen to the tissues and to remove the carbon dioxide. When exercise stops, heart rate and breathing rate return to normal resting rates. Sometimes this can take a while as the body recovers.

Investigating the Effects of Exercise

To measure the effects of exercise on your heart and breathing rates you should:

1. Record your resting heart and breathing rates per minute for a short period of time (e.g. five minutes).
2. Exercise for a short period of time (e.g. five minutes) and record your heart and breathing rate per minute during this time.
3. Rest for a short period of time until your heart and breathing rates return to normal (e.g. five minutes). Record your heart and breathing rates per minute during this time.
4. Draw a graph of your results similar to the one above.

Anaerobic Respiration

During vigorous exercise, the lungs and the blood cannot always deliver enough oxygen to the muscle cells to respire the available glucose aerobically and meet their energy requirements.

When this happens, the glucose can only be partly broken down, releasing a much smaller amount of energy (only about $\frac{1}{20}$ of the energy produced by aerobic respiration). This process is called **anaerobic respiration**.

Anaerobic respiration produces a little bit of energy very quickly, but most of the glucose is changed to **lactic acid**, a waste product.

Glucose	→	Energy Lactic acid

- **Glucose** is brought to the muscle cells by the bloodstream.
- **Lactic acid** gradually builds up in the muscles, making them feel tired and 'rubbery'. It can lead to cramp.
- **Energy** – a small amount of energy is produced quickly and is used for explosive activity.

Excess Post-Exercise Oxygen Consumption

The build-up of lactic acid causes acute fatigue in the muscles and results in **excess post-exercise oxygen consumption** (EPOC). This causes the muscles to stop contracting efficiently. This used to be called '**oxygen debt**'.

After exercise, the lactic acid must be broken down quickly to avoid cell damage; the oxygen debt must be 'repaid' through deep breathing. This provides enough oxygen to convert the lactic acid into carbon dioxide and water. This releases the remainder of the energy that was stored in the glucose originally. While this is happening, your heart rate and breathing rate remain high.

Structure of a Leaf

Leaves are broad, thin and flat with lots of internal air spaces. This creates a **large surface area** and makes them efficient at **photosynthesising**. They are filled with specialised **palisade cells**, which contain lots of **chloroplasts**. Chloroplasts contain **chlorophyll**, which absorbs light for photosynthesis. On the bottom of leaves there are many tiny pores called **stomata**. These allow carbon dioxide into the leaves and oxygen out of them.

Palisade cells contain lots of chloroplasts for photosynthesis

A waxy layer on the top of the leaf stops transpiration (see page 16)

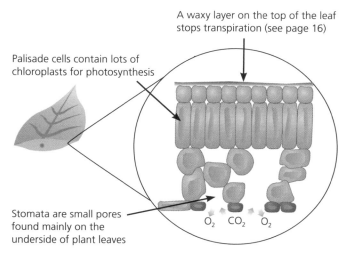

Stomata are small pores found mainly on the underside of plant leaves

O_2 CO_2 O_2

Photosynthesis

Plants make their own food (glucose) by the process of **photosynthesis**. Photosynthesis means 'making through light'. It occurs in the **chloroplasts** of the cells of green plants that are exposed to light (mainly in the leaves).

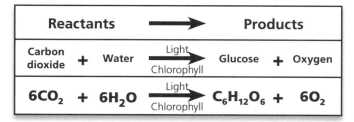

Reactants	→	Products
Carbon dioxide + Water $\xrightarrow[\text{Chlorophyll}]{\text{Light}}$ Glucose + Oxygen		
$6CO_2 + 6H_2O \xrightarrow[\text{Chlorophyll}]{\text{Light}} C_6H_{12}O_6 + 6O_2$		

After the glucose has been made in photosynthesis it is:
- used in respiration
- stored as starch
- made into cellulose cell walls
- made into proteins.

The glucose is transported around plants in specialised cells called **phloem**.

Factors Affecting Photosynthesis

Temperature, carbon dioxide concentration and **light intensity** interact to affect the rate of photosynthesis. Any one of them, at a particular time, may be the **limiting factor**.

Effect of Temperature

1 As the temperature rises so does the rate of photosynthesis. This means temperature is limiting the rate of photosynthesis.

2 As the temperature exceeds about 45°C, the enzymes controlling photosynthesis start to be denatured and the rate of photosynthesis drops to zero.

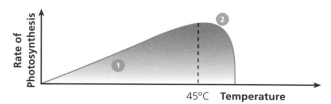

Effect of Carbon Dioxide Concentration

1 As the carbon dioxide concentration rises so does the rate of photosynthesis. So carbon dioxide is limiting the rate of photosynthesis.

2 The rise in carbon dioxide levels now has no effect. Carbon dioxide is no longer the limiting factor. Light or temperature must now be the limiting factor.

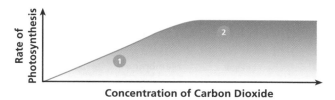

Effect of Light Intensity

1 As the light intensity increases so does the rate of photosynthesis. This means light intensity is limiting the rate of photosynthesis.

2 The rise in light intensity now has no effect. Light is no longer the limiting factor. Carbon dioxide or temperature must now be the limiting factor.

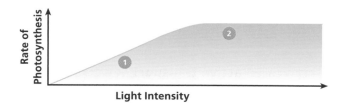

Investigating the Factors that Affect Photosynthesis

The rate at which plants photosynthesise can be investigated using *Elodea* pondweed. When in solution, the rate at which it produces bubbles of oxygen tells us how rapidly it is photosynthesising.

You can investigate the effects of light intensity by moving a table lamp progressively closer to the pondweed and counting the bubbles released. You can see the effects of increasing carbon dioxide by adding sodium hydrogencarbonate and counting the bubbles. You can see the effects of temperature by raising or lowering the temperature and counting the bubbles. The pondweed takes a few minutes to adjust to new conditions, so factor this into your method.

Plant Roots, Osmosis and Active Transport

Water enters plants through their roots. Most of the water is absorbed by the **root hair cells** by a process called **osmosis**. Osmosis is the diffusion of water molecules from an area of **higher concentration** of water to an area of **lower concentration** of water through a **partially permeable membrane**. The root hair cell membranes are partially permeable because they allow water across them but do not allow the solute (sugar) to move from inside the cell.

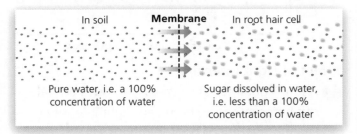

In soil	**Membrane**	In root hair cell
Pure water, i.e. a 100% concentration of water		Sugar dissolved in water, i.e. less than a 100% concentration of water

Plants are adapted to take up water by having many root hair cells. The hair-like structures in root hair cells provide a large surface area to take up water.

Mineral salts are also taken in by the plant's roots. As the concentration of mineral salts is often higher in plants than in the soil, energy is needed to do this. This is called **active transport**; it works against the concentration gradient.

Investigating Osmosis in a Potato

To investigate osmosis you could do the following:

1. Cut out, dry off and measure accurately the mass of some small pieces of potato.
2. Place one piece of potato in a beaker of distilled water for 15 minutes.
3. Remove, dry off the potato and measure its mass.
4. Repeat using sugar solutions of various concentrations instead of distilled water.

The potato in the beaker of distilled water should have gained mass as water entered it by osmosis. The potato pieces in the sugar solutions should have lost mass as water left them by osmosis (unless one solution is the same concentration as the potato, in which case no mass would be lost). More water should have left the potato in more concentrated sugar solutions.

Xylem and Transpiration

Water enters plants through their roots and is transported to the cells in long tube-like structures called **xylem**. Water moves up through these tubes against gravity. The plant does not use any energy to do this. The water moves because of a process called **transpiration**.

1. Water evaporates from the internal leaf cells through the stomata.
2. Water passes from the xylem vessels to leaf cells due to osmosis.
3. This 'pulls' the entire 'thread' of water in that vessel upwards by a very small amount.
4. Water enters xylem from root tissue to replace water that has moved upwards.
5. Water enters root hair cells by osmosis to replace water that has entered the xylem.

The rate at which water is lost through leaves by transpiration is affected by the:

- temperature (warmer means more loss)
- humidity (less humid means more loss)
- wind (more wind means more loss)
- light intensity (brighter light means more loss).

Investigating Organisms in their Environment

Biodiversity is a measure of the variety of different types of organism in a habitat or ecosystem. To investigate this, or how abundant any organisms are in their habitats, **sampling** can be used.

Sampling is when a smaller section of the habitat is investigated and conclusions about the whole habitat are drawn from this. In an ideal investigation all the organisms in a habitat would be counted but this is often not possible or too time consuming.

Most sampling is **random**. This means that chance is used to determine where to look in the habitat. Normally, random numbers would be used as coordinates to investigate the habitat. However, under some circumstances, **systematic sampling** is used.

Systematic sampling is not random. An example of when this type of sampling would be used is when investigating differences in plant numbers and/or varieties in a dry field that turns into a marshy wetland. Sampling would be done at equal distances along a line that runs from the dry land to the wet. This line is called a **transect**.

Using Quadrats for Sampling

Random and systematic sampling can be carried out using a **quadrat**. A quadrat is a square frame, which is placed on the ground to count the number and/or variety of plants or small animals inside it. A suitable size of quadrat should be chosen (commonly $0.25m^2$), and it should be decided how many times it will be placed. Ideally it would be placed a large number of times (to make the data more reliable), but there is balance to be drawn with this and the time-frame available.

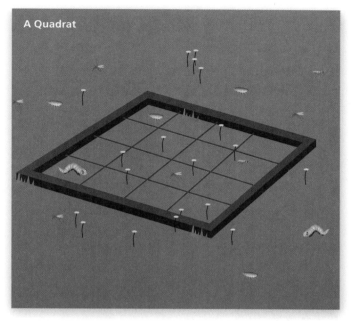

A Quadrat

Counting the number of different species in the quadrats will determine the **species richness** or **frequency** (a measure of biodiversity). Counting the number of individuals of each species will determine the **species density**. This information can be presented per square metre or the results can be multiplied up to estimate the population of the species in the entire habitat.

It is not always possible to count the number of certain plants and animals in quadrats (e.g. the number of grass plants if you were sampling a lawn). In situations like these, you can estimate the **percentage cover** of the organism within the quadrat (i.e. the percentage of the quadrat that it has taken up).

Common examples of using quadrats in schools investigate:

- how many species of plant live on the school field that is regularly mown compared with an area of grass that isn't
- how many species of plant live in shaded areas compared with those in the sun.

Other Sampling Methods

Not all animals stay still to be sampled. If they move, special equipment and techniques are needed to catch them and estimate their total populations.

A **pitfall trap** is used to catch small animals. It is a small container, which is buried in the ground. Animals fall in and are trapped. Sometimes the container is filled with food to attract animals.

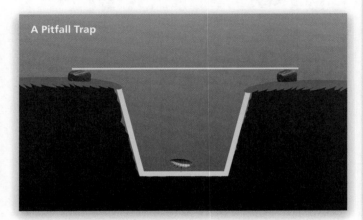

A Pitfall Trap

Sweep netting uses a giant net that is swept through undergrowth to capture insects. Different types of vegetation require a slightly different technique in sweeping.

Pond nets are similar in design and can be used to sample aquatic habitats.

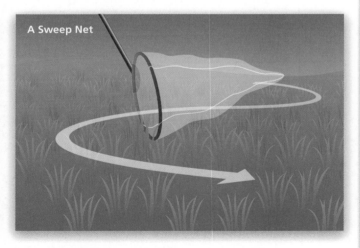

A Sweep Net

Kick sampling is an effective way of sampling organisms living on the bottom of a stream. A net is placed downstream and the stream bed is gently disturbed by kicking it. As the organisms are swept downstream they are caught in the net.

Pooters are small devices used to collect insects. They consist of a jar with two tubes attached. When one tube is sucked, the insects are pulled down the other tube into the jar and not the person's mouth.

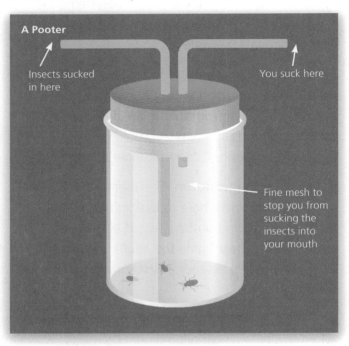

A Pooter

Insects sucked in here

You suck here

Fine mesh to stop you from sucking the insects into your mouth

To estimate the number of mobile animals in a habitat, the **mark**, **release**, **recapture** method can be used. Any organisms that are caught are marked in a way that will not harm them. They are then freed to be caught again during random sampling. The number caught that are marked, compared with the number unmarked, can be used to estimate the total population.

Monitoring the Environment

To deepen your understanding of the way in which animals and plants live in a habitat you might want to measure:
- temperature
- pH
- light intensity.

This can be done using a thermometer and a pH indicator as frequently as needed.

However, many scientists now use electronic equipment connected to a small computer to do the same thing much more frequently and often more accurately. This is called **data logging**.

B2 Topic 3: Common Systems

This topic looks at:
- fossils and the fossil record
- the composition of the blood
- the circulatory and digestive systems

Anatomy of the Pentadactyl Limb

The anatomy of the **pentadactyl limb** is often used by scientists as evidence for evolution. The pentadactyl limb is a pattern of limb bones found in all classes of **tetrapods** (vertebrate animals with four legs, which includes amphibians and mammals). The pentadactyl limb includes the following bones (in a forearm):

- one proximal bone (humerus)
- two distal bones (radius and ulna)
- several carpals (wrist bones)
- five metacarpals (palm bones)
- many phalanges (digit bones).

Many tetrapods have slightly different arrangements of these bones, which suit their habitat or behaviour:

- Monkeys have much longer forearms with hands that can grasp to swing through trees.
- Horses have a much longer third metacarpal, which has a hoof to allow them to run fast.
- Bats have four long metacarpals that have turned into a wing, with one shorter digit remaining to allow them to hang.

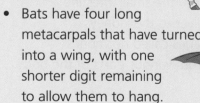
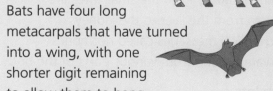

The similarity of this arrangement of bones in all tetrapods indicates that they have evolved from a single ancestor.

Fossils and the Fossil Record

Fossils are the imprints or remains of living organisms from millions of years ago, found in **sedimentary rocks**. They allow us to see the anatomy of species that are now extinct and also provide evidence of how organisms have evolved. However, the **fossil record** is **incomplete** because:

- some body tissues do not fossilise (the soft bits decay)
- many fossils have not yet been discovered
- fossils do not always form.

Despite this, gradual changes in the fossil record confirm that species have changed over long periods of time, providing strong evidence for evolution.

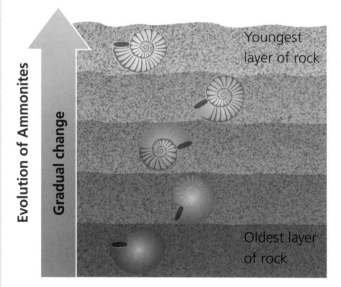

Growth

Growth is a permanent increase in the size of an organism. There are three types that contribute to the growth and development of organisms:

1 **Cell division**: the process in which two cells are formed from one (see mitosis, page 7).

2 **Cell elongation**: the process in which cells, mainly in plants, elongate (stretch out). The actual cells get bigger, rather than reproduce.

3 **Cell differentiation**: the process through which an undifferentiated (unspecialised) cell can become a specific type of cell (see page 9).

Measuring Growth

Although **length** (or height) is often used as a measure of growth (in plants and humans), it is not very accurate because it does not take into account growth in other directions, e.g. an increase in girth or width. Growth is better measured by finding the **total mass** of an organism.

The best, and most accurate, way of doing this is to measure the **dry mass**. However, this can only be done when the organism is dead, because it involves gently heating the organism in an oven until all the water has evaporated out of it. As a result, **wet mass** is usually used as an alternative measure of growth. Measuring wet mass means measuring the total mass of a living organism.

Plants and animals grow in different ways:
- Plants continue to grow throughout their lives in height and width.
- Most animals grow quickly at first before slowing down. They eventually stop growing.

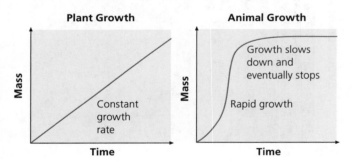

Growth percentiles are determined from growth charts of organisms to compare the growth of an individual with the growth of others of the same species. This allows changes in growth to be tracked over time. Normal growth of average organisms remains near the 50th percentile. Any increase in percentile values shows a greater than average growth. The reverse applies. Percentile charts are usually used to measure the growth of young children.

Composition of the Blood

Blood has four components:

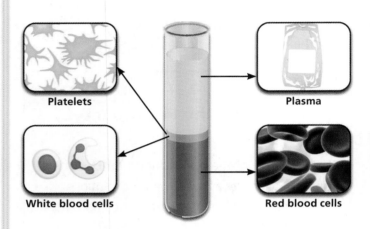

Red Blood Cells
- Red blood cells have no nucleus so that they can be packed with **haemoglobin.**
- The biconcave shape of the cells provides a bigger surface area through which to absorb oxygen.
- Haemoglobin combines easily with oxygen. In the lungs, where there is lots of oxygen:

haemoglobin + oxygen $\rightarrow$ oxyhaemoglobin

In the tissues where oxygen is being used up:

oxyhaemoglobin $\rightarrow$ haemoglobin + oxygen

- Haemoglobin's reversible reaction with oxygen ensures oxygen is transported to where it is needed.

Plasma
Plasma is a straw-coloured liquid consisting mainly of water. It transports:
- carbon dioxide from the organs to the lungs
- soluble products of digestion (e.g. glucose and amino acids) from the small intestine
- urea from the liver to the kidneys
- chemical messages called hormones
- water to and from various parts of the body.

Platelets
Platelets are tiny particles found in blood plasma. They are not cells and do not have a nucleus. They are very important in helping the blood to clot when a blood vessel has been damaged or cut.

White Blood Cells

White blood cells are part of the immune system. They defend the body from attack from pathogens.

There are two types of white blood cell, which are:
- phagocytes
- lymphocytes.

Phagocytes form part of the body's non-specific (or innate) immune response against pathogens (microorganisms). Phagocytes engulf and destroy these microorganisms and eventually die, forming pus.

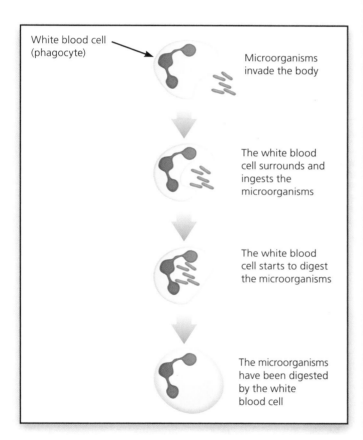

White blood cell (phagocyte)

Microorganisms invade the body

The white blood cell surrounds and ingests the microorganisms

The white blood cell starts to digest the microorganisms

The microorganisms have been digested by the white blood cell

Lymphocytes form part of our specific (or adaptive) immune response. They recognise the microorganisms as **antigens** (foreign bodies) and produce **antibodies** to destroy them (often by making them clump together). We feel ill because it takes time for the white blood cells to produce antibodies to kill the microorganisms.

The production of antibodies is much faster if a person has already had the infectious disease. The white blood cells 'remember' the antigen and, in the future, can produce antibodies more rapidly,

providing the person with **natural immunity**.

White blood cells also produce anti-toxins, which neutralise harmful **toxins** produced by microorganisms.

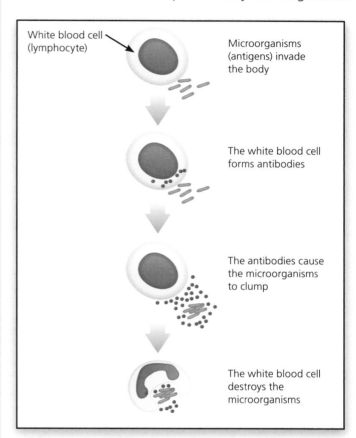

White blood cell (lymphocyte)

Microorganisms (antigens) invade the body

The white blood cell forms antibodies

The antibodies cause the microorganisms to clump

The white blood cell destroys the microorganisms

Cells, Tissues, Organs and Systems

The human body is made from millions of individual cells. But the arrangement of these cells is not random. Cells that carry out the same function are often arranged together into tissues, organs, and organ systems.

Tissues are groups of specialised cells of the same type that complete a specific function. Examples are muscle tissue in animals and palisade tissue in plants (see page 15).

Organs are groups of tissues that are joined together to complete a specific function. Examples are hearts in animals and leaves in plants.

Organ systems are groups of organs that work together to complete a specific function. Examples are the circulatory system (see page 22) and digestive system (see page 25) in animals.

The Circulatory System

The **circulatory system** is the body's transport system. It transports the following:

- oxygen and glucose
- carbon dioxide and water
- nutrients
- hormones.

However, primarily, it carries blood from the heart to all the cells of the body to provide them with glucose and oxygen, and carries waste products including carbon dioxide away from the cells. Blood is pumped to the lungs so that carbon dioxide can be exchanged for oxygen. The system consists of the **heart**, the **blood vessels** and the **blood**.

The Double Circulation

There are two 'loops' in the circulatory system. One loop carries blood from the heart to the lungs and then back to the heart, and another loop carries blood from the heart to all other parts of the body and then back to the heart.

This means that blood flows around a 'figure of eight' and passes through the heart twice on each circuit. This is called **double circulation**. Blood travels away from the heart through the **arteries** and returns to the heart through the **veins**.

The left side of the heart pumps blood that is rich in oxygen, and delivers it to all other parts of the body.

The right side of the heart pumps blood that is low in oxygen to the lungs, to pick up oxygen.

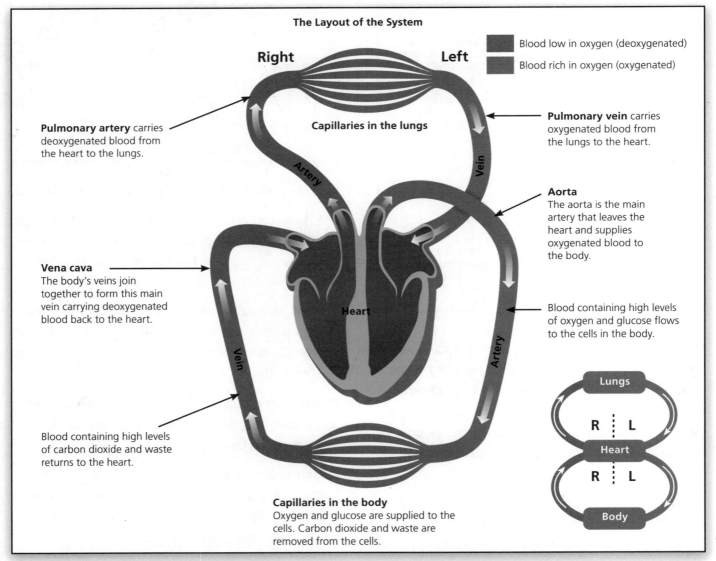

The Layout of the System

Right | Left

Blood low in oxygen (deoxygenated)
Blood rich in oxygen (oxygenated)

Capillaries in the lungs

Pulmonary artery carries deoxygenated blood from the heart to the lungs.

Pulmonary vein carries oxygenated blood from the lungs to the heart.

Aorta
The aorta is the main artery that leaves the heart and supplies oxygenated blood to the body.

Vena cava
The body's veins join together to form this main vein carrying deoxygenated blood back to the heart.

Heart

Blood containing high levels of oxygen and glucose flows to the cells in the body.

Blood containing high levels of carbon dioxide and waste returns to the heart.

Lungs

R | L

Heart

R | L

Body

Capillaries in the body
Oxygen and glucose are supplied to the cells. Carbon dioxide and waste are removed from the cells.

The Heart

The **heart** is the main organ in the circulatory system. It pumps blood around the body.

- Most of the walls of the heart are made from muscle.
- **Atria** are the smaller, less muscular upper chambers, which receive blood coming back to the heart through veins.
- **Ventricles** are the larger, more muscular lower chambers. The left is more muscular than the right since it has to pump blood around the whole body (not just to the lungs).
- **Valves** make sure that the blood flows in the right direction, and cannot flow backwards.

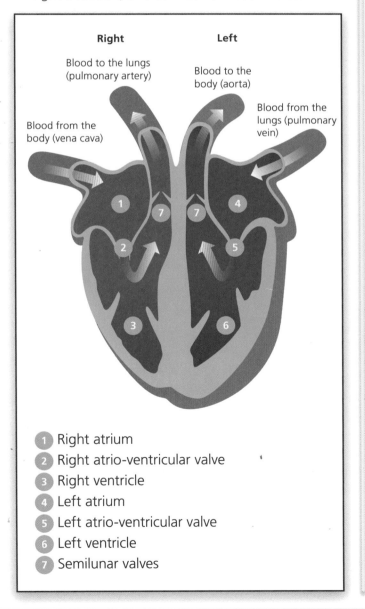

Right   Left

Blood to the lungs (pulmonary artery)

Blood to the body (aorta)

Blood from the body (vena cava)

Blood from the lungs (pulmonary vein)

1 Right atrium
2 Right atrio-ventricular valve
3 Right ventricle
4 Left atrium
5 Left atrio-ventricular valve
6 Left ventricle
7 Semilunar valves

How The Heart Pumps Blood

When the atria contract, blood is forced through the atrio-ventricular valves and down into the ventricles.

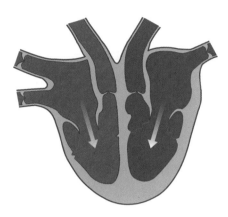

When the ventricles contract, the atrio-ventricular valves snap shut, forcing the blood upwards to the aorta (to the body) and pulmonary artery (to the lungs).

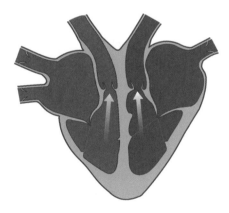

When the heart muscle relaxes, blood flows into the atria from the veins. The semilunar valves stop blood coming backwards from the arteries.

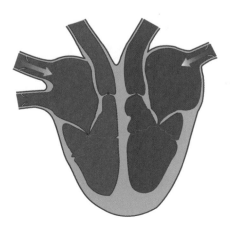

The Blood Vessels

There are three types of blood vessels – arteries, veins and capillaries. They form the 'plumbing' of the circulatory system.

Arteries

- Thick, elastic wall containing many muscle fibres to cope with blood under much higher pressure.
- Much smaller lumen compared with the thickness of the wall.
- No valves.
- Carry blood away from the heart.
- Only arteries display a pulse, which is a pressure wave due to the elasticity of the artery wall.

Veins

- Thinner, less elastic wall containing fewer muscle fibres as blood is at low pressure.
- Much bigger lumen compared with the thickness of the wall.
- Have valves to prevent backflow of blood.
- Carry blood towards the heart.

Capillaries

- Narrow, thin-walled vessels, just one cell thick.
- Microscopic (too small to see without a microscope).
- Exchange of substances between cells and blood only takes place in the capillaries.
- Connect arteries to veins through tissues and organs.

Exchange of Substances at the Capillaries

Arteries branch into tiny one cell thick capillaries, which pass close to each cell before reuniting to form a vein. Only at the capillaries can substances be exchanged with the body's cells. Glucose and oxygen diffuse from the blood to the cells and carbon dioxide and other waste diffuse from the cells to the blood.

Similarly, carbon dioxide diffuses from the blood capillaries into the alveoli in the lungs, while oxygen diffuses from the alveoli into the capillaries.

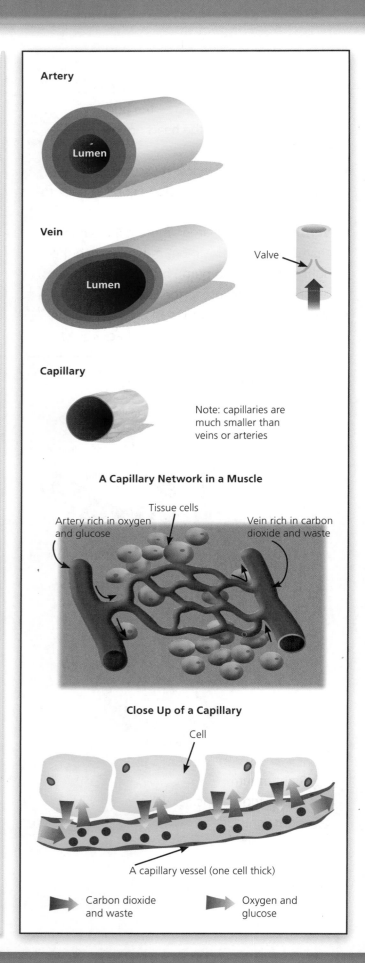

Artery

Lumen

Vein

Lumen

Valve

Capillary

Note: capillaries are much smaller than veins or arteries

A Capillary Network in a Muscle

Tissue cells

Artery rich in oxygen and glucose

Vein rich in carbon dioxide and waste

Close Up of a Capillary

Cell

A capillary vessel (one cell thick)

Carbon dioxide and waste

Oxygen and glucose

The Digestive System

The **digestive system** is made up of a long muscular tube in which enzymes speed up (catalyse) the breakdown of large insoluble molecules, e.g. starch, proteins and fats, into smaller soluble molecules so that they can pass through the walls of the small intestine and into the blood. Absorption of water takes place in the large intestine. This leaves only indigestible food, which leaves the body as faeces via the anus.

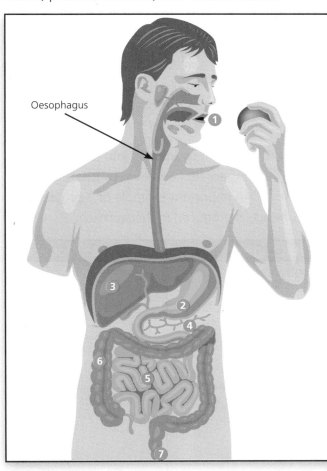

Oesophagus

1. **Mouth** – contains teeth for mechanical breakdown of food. Produces the enzyme carbohydrase.
2. **Stomach** – produces the enzyme protease, and also hydrochloric acid, which kills bacteria, and also provides the ideal conditions for protease.
3. **Liver** – produces bile, which helps fat digestion.
4. **Pancreas** – produces all three enzymes carbohydrase, protease and lipase.
5. **Small intestine** – small soluble molecules (broken down food, vitamins and minerals) are absorbed into the blood here. Produces all three enzymes carbohydrase, protease and lipase.
6. **Large intestine** – excess water, from the contents of the intestines, is reabsorbed into the blood here.
7. **Anus** – the remaining indigestible food makes up the faeces, which leave the body here.

HT Small Intestine

The small intestine is covered by millions of small finger-like projections called **villi**, each of which contains a network of capillaries (see page 24). These help efficient absorption of small, soluble molecules by:

- providing a very large surface area
- providing a huge blood supply to carry away nutrients
- having a single layer of cells between the intestine and the blood to allow nutrients to diffuse easily.

Villi Lining the Wall of the Small Intestine

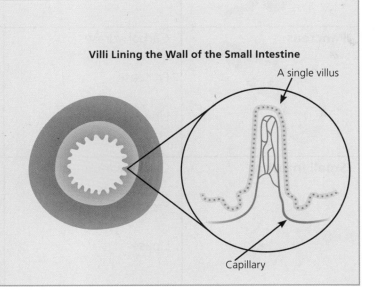

A single villus

Capillary

Moving Food by Peristalsis

To move food along the oesophagus and small intestine, the muscles that line the walls of these tube-shaped organs relax in front of the food and contract behind it. This relaxation and contraction occurs in rhythmic waves carrying the food along. This is called **peristalsis**.

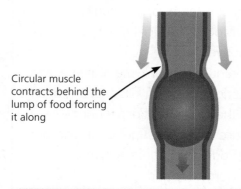

Circular muscle contracts behind the lump of food forcing it along

Enzymes in the Digestive System

Enzymes are biological catalysts (see page 11). In the digestive system enzymes are produced in the mouth, the stomach, the pancreas and the small intestine. They digest **carbohydrates**, **fats** and **proteins** into small, soluble molecules that can be absorbed into the blood in the small intestine.

Carbohydrates (e.g. starch) are broken down by **carbohydrases** into simple sugars (e.g. glucose). An important example of a carbohydrase is **amylase**, which is found in the saliva of the mouth.

Fats are broken down by **lipases** into fatty acids and glycerol. Proteins are broken down by **proteases** into amino acids. An important example of a protease is pepsin, which is produced in the stomach.

Enzyme Source	Enzyme	What it Digests	Molecules Produced
Salivary glands	Carbohydrase	Carbohydrates	Sugars (e.g. glucose)
Stomach	Protease	Proteins	Amino acids
Pancreas	Carbohydrase	Carbohydrates	Sugars (e.g. glucose)
	Protease	Proteins	Amino acids
	Lipase	Lipids (fats and oils)	Fatty acids and glycerol
Small intestine	Carbohydrase	Carbohydrates	Sugars (e.g. glucose)
	Protease	Proteins	Amino acids
	Lipase	Lipids (fats and oils)	Fatty acids and glycerol

The Role of Bile

Bile is produced in the **liver** and then stored in the **gall bladder** before being released into the small intestine.

Bile has two functions:

1. It neutralises the acid, which was added to food in the stomach, to produce alkaline conditions in which the enzymes of the small intestine work best.
2. It emulsifies fats, i.e. it breaks down large drops of fat into small droplets to increase their surface area. This enables the lipase enzymes to work much faster.

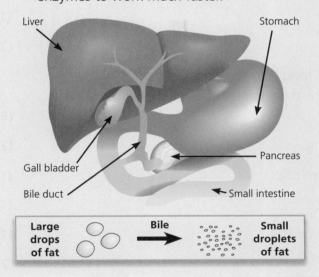

Using Visking Tubing to Model the Digestive System

Visking tubing can be used to model the walls of the digestive system, through which only small molecules can be absorbed. Visking tubing will allow glucose to pass through, but not the larger molecule, starch.

1. Fill a short length of Visking tubing with starch solution and place in a beaker of water.
2. Test the surrounding water solution with iodine to prove that starch cannot pass through.
3. Fill a second short length of Visking tubing with starch and add some amylase enzyme before placing in a beaker of water. The amylase should break down the starch into glucose.
4. Test the surrounding water solution again with iodine to prove that starch cannot pass through.
5. Test the water for glucose using Benedict's solution to prove that glucose can pass through.

This experiment can be completed using different concentrations of enzymes to determine which is the most effective.

Functional Foods

Prebiotics are non-digestible functional foods. They stimulate the growth and development of 'beneficial bacteria' that are found naturally in the human gut (i.e. in the small intestine and the large intestine). The growth and development of beneficial bacteria results in health benefits.

An example of a type of prebiotic is oligosaccharides. Naturally found in onions and leeks, oligosaccharides are short-chain carbohydrates.

Probiotics are foods that contain live microorganisms that are thought to be beneficial to the consumer. The lactic acid bacteria *Lactobacillus* and *Bifidobacterium* are examples of bacteria found in probiotics.

Naturally found in very small amounts, **plant stanol esters** are produced commercially by using bacteria to convert plant sterols (a type of fat) into stanols.

Plant stanol esters can lower cholesterol, which reduces the risk of heart disease. Food manufacturers add plant stanol esters to products such as spreads (e.g. margarine) so that they can promote them as being healthy.

Some scientists think that the effects of functional foods on the digestive system are not as good as some food manufacturers might suggest.

Questions labelled with an asterisk (*) are ones where the quality of your written communication will be assessed – you should take particular care with your spelling, punctuation and grammar, as well as the clarity of expression, on these questions.

1 **(a)** Describe the function of two components present in plant cells that are not found in animal cells. **(4)**

(b) (i) State the reaction that occurs in mitochondria. **(1)**

(ii) State a type of cell in which you might expect to find many mitochondria. **(1)**

2 Describe the structure of DNA. **(3)**

3 State the definition of the term 'genetic engineering'. **(1)**

4 Describe how herbicide-resistant crops have been produced. **(4)**

5 **(a)** During fertilisation, a sperm cell and an egg cell fuse to form

A ☐ an embryo   **C** ☐ a diploid zygote

B ☐ a haploid zygote   **D** ☐ a clone **(1)**

(b) Suggest three ethical concerns about cloning. **(3)**

*(c) Describe the differences between mitosis and meiosis. Include in your answer where it happens, the number of cells made, how many chromosomes the daughter cells have and whether or not they are identical. **(6)**

6 **(a)** Suggest why stem cells might be important in medicine. **(2)**

(b) Suggest an ethical concern about using embryonic stem cells. **(1)**

7 **(a)** State what proteins are made from. **(1)**

(b) State what substance the code to make proteins is stored in. **(1)**

(c) State what proteins are used for in the body. **(2)**

8 **(a)** Describe how enzymes function. Use the lock and key hypothesis in your answer. **(3)**

(b) State the two ways in which enzymes can be denatured. **(2)**

(c) Describe how enzymes are denatured. Use the lock and key hypothesis in your answer. **(2)**

9 **(a)** State the word equation for aerobic respiration. **(2)**

(b) State the definition of the term 'diffusion'. **(1)**

(c) State the word equation for anaerobic respiration. **(2)**

(d) Explain why excess post-exercise oxygen consumption occurs. **(1)**

10 **(a)** Explain how leaves are adapted for photosynthesis. **(2)**

(b) State the word equation for photosynthesis. **(2)**

(c) State the definition of the term 'osmosis'. **(1)**

11 Describe water transport in plants. **(4)**

12 **(a)** Which of the following is used to catch small animals? Food is sometimes placed inside it.

  A ☐ a pitfall trap   **C** ☐ a pooter

  B ☐ a net   **D** ☐ a quadrat   **(1)**

  (b) State the definition of the term 'biodiversity'. **(1)**

  (c) Describe how quadrats are used for sampling. **(3)**

13 White blood cells are a component of our blood.

  (a) State the other three components of the blood. **(3)**

  (b) State the two types of white blood cell. **(2)**

14 State the definitions of the terms 'tissues', 'organs' and 'systems'. **(3)**

15 **(a)** Explain the term 'double circulation'. **(1)**

  *__(b)** Describe the journey of the blood around the body, starting at the left ventricle. Include the names of the blood vessels in your answer. **(6)**

  (c) Explain how arteries, veins and capillaries are adapted for their function. **(3)**

  (d) State the substances that are frequently exchanged between the blood in the capillaries and the tissues. Include the direction of the exchange in your answer. **(4)**

16 **(a)** State the functions of two sections of the digestive system. **(4)**

  (b) Describe the process of peristalsis. **(1)**

  (c) State the three enzymes produced in the digestive system. **(3)**

HT

17 **(a)** Describe the main achievement of the Human Genome Project (HGP). **(1)**

  (b) Suggest two uses of the findings of the HGP. **(2)**

  (c) Suggest a concern regarding the HGP. **(1)**

18 *Dolly the sheep was the first cloned mammal. Describe in detail how mammals are cloned. **(6)**

19 Describe how protein synthesis occurs. **(5)**

20 Explain how the pentadactyl limb is used as evidence for evolution. **(3)**

21 **(a)** Describe how the small intestine is adapted for its function. **(4)**

  (b) (i) State where bile is produced. **(1)**

    (ii) State the two roles of bile. **(2)**

The History of the Periodic Table

All things are made of elements. The known elements are arranged in the **periodic table**. However, the periodic table is a relatively recent invention.
- Before they knew about chemical elements, some early scientists described things as being made from fire, air, earth and water.
- The idea of elements was first mentioned in the mid-1600s.

Before the modern periodic table was developed, a number of attempts were made to arrange the elements. However, it was not until 1869 that Russian chemist **Dmitri Mendeleev** developed the modern periodic table.
- He arranged the elements in order of atomic mass.
- The table included all the known elements and left gaps for those not yet discovered.
- Each element was put into the group (column) where its properties fitted best.
- Elements that did not fit were put into a spare column.

Using his periodic table, Mendeleev was able to predict the existence and properties of undiscovered elements. One of these was silicon, which was discovered many years later and matched the predictions.

The modern periodic table can also be used to predict the properties of artificial elements (those that do not occur naturally).

The Periodic Table

Elements are the building blocks of all materials. The 100 or so elements are arranged in the periodic table, in order of increasing atomic number. The elements are arranged in rows (**periods**) so that elements with similar properties are in the same column (**group**). This forms the basis of the periodic table (a detailed version is on page 103).

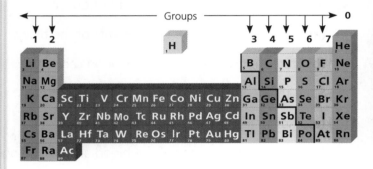

- More than three-quarters of the elements are metals; the rest are non-metals.
- Metals are found mainly in Groups 1 and 2 and in the central block.
- Group 1 elements are known as the **alkali metals**.
- Group 7 elements are known as the **halogens**.
- Group 0 elements are known as the **noble gases**.
- The **transition metals** are in the central block between Group 2 and Group 3.

Trends in the Periodic Table

- The elements in a particular group have similar chemical properties since they have the same number of electrons in their outermost shells.
- The mass of elements gets bigger as you go from left to right across a period (row).
- Elements in Group 1 (which all have 1 electron in their outermost shell) become more reactive as you go down the group.
- Elements in Group 7 (which all have 7 electrons in their outermost shell) become less reactive as you go down the group.
- Elements in Group 0 all have a full outermost electron shell. All these elements are unreactive.

The Atom

Elements are made up of **atoms**. An atom has a nucleus that contains the subatomic particles **protons** and **neutrons** (the exception is hydrogen, which does not contain neutrons). The nucleus is surrounded by orbiting electrons arranged in shells. These particles have different relative masses and charges.

Subatomic Particle	Relative Mass	Relative Charge
Proton	1	+1 (positive)
Neutron	1	0 (neutral)
Electron	Negligible	−1 (negative)

An atom has the same number of protons as electrons, so the atom as a whole has no electrical charge. All the atoms of a particular element have:
- the same number of protons in their nuclei
- the same number of electrons orbiting the nucleus.

A Representation of a Helium Atom

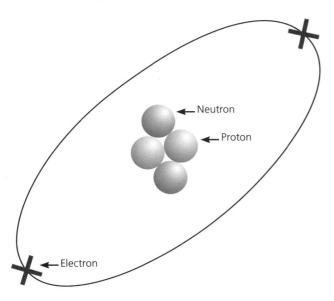

← Neutron

← Proton

← Electron

Atomic Number and Mass Number

Each element in the periodic table has two numbers next to its symbol, for example:

Lithium

$^{7}_{3}\text{Li}$

Nitrogen

$^{14}_{7}\text{N}$

Iron

$^{56}_{26}\text{Fe}$

The number at the bottom is the **atomic number**. This gives the number of protons found in the nucleus of an atom of that element. It also gives the number of electrons orbiting the nucleus, because all atoms have no overall electrical charge.

The number at the top is the **mass number**.

The mass number tells you the total number of protons and neutrons there are in the nucleus of an atom of the element.

Element	Atomic Number	Mass Number
Lithium (nucleus contains 3 protons and 4 neutrons)	3	7
Nitrogen (nucleus contains 7 protons and 7 neutrons)	7	14
Iron (nucleus contains 26 protons and 30 neutrons)	26	56

Relative Atomic Mass

The actual mass of a single atom is far too small to be used easily in calculations. To make things more manageable we use **relative atomic mass**.

Relative atomic mass is the mass of a particular atom compared to $\frac{1}{12}$ of the mass of a carbon atom.

Isotopes

The number of **protons** in the atom defines the element. All the atoms of a particular element have the same number of protons in their nuclei; this number is unique to each particular element and is its atomic number.

However, atoms of the same element can have different numbers of **neutrons**: these atoms are called **isotopes** of the element.

Because all isotopes of an element have the same number of protons and the same electronic configuration, they have the same chemical properties and so their reactions are the same. They are easy to spot because they have the **same atomic number** but a **different mass number**.

Examples

1 Chlorine has two isotopes.

$$^{35}_{17}\text{Cl} \qquad ^{37}_{17}\text{Cl}$$

17 protons   17 protons
17 electrons   17 electrons
18 neutrons   20 neutrons
(35 − 17 = 18)   (37 − 17 = 20)

2 Hydrogen has three isotopes.

$$^{1}_{1}\text{H} \qquad ^{2}_{1}\text{H} \qquad ^{3}_{1}\text{H}$$

1 proton   1 proton   1 proton
1 electron   1 electron   1 electron
0 neutrons   1 neutron   2 neutrons
(1 − 1 = 0)   (2 − 1 = 1)   (3 − 1 = 2)

3 Carbon has three naturally occurring isotopes.

$$^{12}_{6}\text{C} \qquad ^{13}_{6}\text{C} \qquad ^{14}_{6}\text{C}$$

6 protons   6 protons   6 protons
6 electrons   6 electrons   6 electrons
6 neutrons   7 neutrons   8 neutrons
(12 − 6 = 6)   (13 − 6 = 7)   (14 − 6 = 8)

Relative Atomic Mass

The mass numbers in the examples in column 1 are the atomic masses of each particular isotope of an element. **Relative atomic mass** is a (weighted) average for the different isotopes of an element.

Chemists use relative atomic masses because they take into account the relative isotopic masses and the abundance of each one.

Example 1: Chlorine
Naturally occurring chlorine consists of 75% of $^{35}_{17}\text{Cl}$ and 25% of $^{37}_{17}\text{Cl}$, i.e. in a ratio of 3:1

So, for every four atoms of chlorine, three of them are $^{35}_{17}\text{Cl}$ and one of them is $^{37}_{17}\text{Cl}$.

So the total atomic mass of these four atoms
$= (3 \times 35) + (1 \times 37) = 142$

Therefore, the **relative atomic mass** of chlorine is:

$$\frac{142}{4} = \textbf{35.5}$$

N.B. Relative atomic masses and relative isotopic masses are often not whole numbers but are rounded up or down for display in the periodic table for ease of calculations.

Example 2: Magnesium
Magnesium consists of 80% of $^{24}_{12}\text{Mg}$, 10% of $^{25}_{12}\text{Mg}$ and 10% of $^{26}_{12}\text{Mg}$, i.e. in the ratio of 8:1:1

So, for every ten atoms of magnesium, eight of them are $^{24}_{12}\text{Mg}$, one of them is $^{25}_{12}\text{Mg}$ and one of them is $^{26}_{12}\text{Mg}$.

So the total atomic mass of these ten atoms
$= (8 \times 24) + (1 \times 25) + (1 \times 26) = 243$

Therefore, the **relative atomic mass** of magnesium is:

$$\frac{243}{10} = \textbf{24.3}$$

Electronic Configuration

Electronic configuration shows how the electrons are arranged around the nucleus of an atom in energy levels (shells).

- The electrons in an atom occupy the lowest available shells (i.e. the shells nearest to the nucleus).
- The first shell can only contain a maximum of two electrons.
- The shells after the first shell can each hold a maximum of eight electrons.
- We write electronic configuration as a series of numbers.

Hydrogen, H
Atomic No. = 1
No. of electrons = 1

1

GROUP 3 | GROUP 4 | GROUP 5 | GROUP 6 | GROUP 7 | GROUP 0

Helium, He
Atomic No. = 2
No. of electrons = 2

2

Boron, B
Atomic No. = 5
No. of electrons = 5

2.3

Carbon, C
Atomic No. = 6
No. of electrons = 6

2.4

Nitrogen, N
Atomic No. = 7
No. of electrons = 7

2.5

Oxygen, O
Atomic No. = 8
No. of electrons = 8

2.6

Fluorine, F
Atomic No. = 9
No. of electrons = 9

2.7

Neon, Ne
Atomic No. = 10
No. of electrons = 10

2.8

Aluminium, Al
Atomic No. = 13
No. of electrons = 13

2.8.3

Silicon, Si
Atomic No. = 14
No. of electrons = 14

2.8.4

Phosphorus, P
Atomic No. = 15
No. of electrons = 15

2.8.5

Sulfur, S
Atomic No. = 16
No. of electrons = 16

2.8.6

Chlorine, Cl
Atomic No. = 17
No. of electrons = 17

2.8.7

Argon, Ar
Atomic No. = 18
No. of electrons = 18

2.8.8

GROUP 1 | GROUP 2

Lithium, Li
Atomic No. = 3
No. of electrons = 3

2.1

Beryllium, Be
Atomic No. = 4
No. of electrons = 4

2.2

Sodium, Na
Atomic No. = 11
No. of electrons = 11

2.8.1

Magnesium, Mg
Atomic No. = 12
No. of electrons = 12

2.8.2

Potassium, K
Atomic No. = 19
No. of electrons = 19

2.8.8.1

Calcium, Ca
Atomic No. = 20
No. of electrons = 20

2.8.8.2

The Transition Metals

This table is arranged in order of atomic (proton) number, placing the elements in groups.
Elements in the same group have the same number of electrons in their highest occupied energy level (outer shell).

Notice that there is a connection between the number of outer electrons and the position of an element in a group: elements in Group 1 have only one electron in their outermost shell, elements in Group 2 have only two electrons in their outermost shell, and so on.

Electronic configuration of oxygen is 2.6 because there are:
- 2 electrons in this shell
- 6 electrons in this shell.

Ionic Bonding

To become chemically stable, all atoms (except hydrogen) lose or gain electrons in order to have eight in their outer shell. These electrons must be accepted by, or donated by, other atoms. Sometimes electrons are completely transferred. This results in the formation of an **ionic bond**.

An ionic bond occurs between a **metal atom** and a **non-metal atom** and involves a transfer of electrons from one metal atom to the other non-metal atom, to form electrically charged 'atoms' called **ions**, which may be positively charged **metal ions** or negatively charged **non-metal ions**.

Groups of atoms can also form ions. For example, nitrate ions are negatively charged (NO_3^-) and ammonium ions are positively charged (NH_4^+).

Example 1

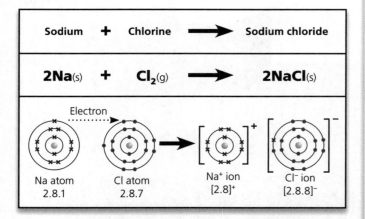

The sodium atom has one electron in its outer shell, which is transferred to the chlorine atom. Both now

have eight electrons in their outer shell (i.e. complete outer shells). The atoms are now ions: Na^+ and Cl^-.

The compound formed is sodium chloride, NaCl.

Example 2

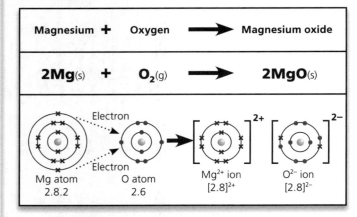

The magnesium atom has two electrons in its outer shell which are transferred to the oxygen atom. Both have eight electrons in their outer shell. The atoms are now ions: Mg^{2+} and O^{2-}.

The compound formed is magnesium oxide, MgO.

Naming Metal Compounds

There are a few general and simple rules to remember when naming metal compounds:
- The metal's name is always written first.
- Change the ending of the name of the non-metal to -ide, but only when there is a single non-metal present.
- If there are two non-metals present and one of them is oxygen, then end the name in -ate.

For example:

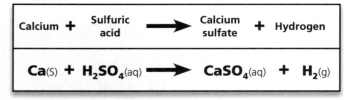

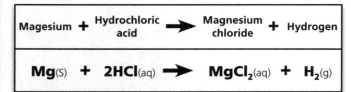

Predicting Formulae

Ionic compounds are neutral because the charges on the ions cancel each other out. Knowing this and the charge on the ions, we can predict formulae for any ionic compound.

Predicting the Formula for Magnesium Chloride

Magnesium ions have a 2+ charge, Mg^{2+}.
Chloride ions have a 1− charge, Cl^-.
The charge on two chloride ions balances out the charge on the magnesium ion: $Mg^{2+} + 2 \times Cl^- = MgCl_2$.
This is the same for any magnesium halide.

Predicting the Formula for Sodium Carbonate

Sodium ions have a 1+ charge, Na^+.
Carbonate ions have a 2- charge, CO_3^{2-}.
The charge on two sodium ions balances out the charge on the carbonate ion: $2 \times Na^+ + CO_3^{2-} = Na_2CO_3$.

Predicting the Formula for Calcium Hydroxide

Calcium ions have a 2+ charge, Ca^{2+}.
Hydroxide ions have a 1- charge, OH^-.
The charge on two hydroxide ions balances out the charge on one calcium ion: $Ca^{2+} + 2 \times OH^- = Ca(OH)_2$.
Brackets ( ) are used to show there are two hydroxide ions in the compound.

Predicting the Formula for Potassium Nitrate

Potassium ions have a 1+ charge, K^+.
Nitrate ions have a 1- charge, NO_3^-.
The charge on one nitrate ion balances out the charge on one potassium ion: $K^+ + NO_3^- = KNO_3$.

Predicting the Formula for Calcium Oxide

Calcium ions have a 2+ charge, Ca^{2+}.
Oxide ions have a 2- charge, O^{2-}.
The charge on one oxide ion balances out the charge on one calcium ion: $Ca^{2+} + O^{2-} = CaO$.

Predicting the Formula for Magnesium Sulfate

Magnesium ions have a 2+ charge, Mg^{2+}.
Sulfate ions have a 2- charge, SO_4^{2-}.
The charge on one sulfate ion balances out the charge on one magnesium ion: $Mg^{2+} + SO_4^{2-} = MgSO_4$.

Properties of Ionic Compounds

Ionic compounds such as sodium chloride and magnesium oxide have high melting and boiling points and conduct electricity when molten or in solution.

 Sodium chloride consists of a giant lattice held together by the strong electrostatic forces of attraction between the positive (sodium) ions, and the negative (chloride) ions. These strong electrostatic forces are the ionic bonds.

 — Negatively charged chloride ions

+ Positively charged sodium ions

Magnesium oxide consists of a similar giant lattice made up of Mg^{2+} and O^{2-} ions. Both of these compounds are examples of binary salts, which contain two elements, although all salts are made of positive and negative ions. Ionic compounds have high melting and boiling points due to the strong electrostatic forces of attraction that hold them together. They conduct electricity when molten or in solution because the charged ions are free to move between the electrodes and act as a current.

Solubility of Ionic Compounds

Some ionic compounds are soluble in water because the water can shield the electrostatic forces of attraction between the positive and negative ions. There are some general rules that can be used to help determine if an ionic compound is soluble in water.

The following are **soluble** in water.
- All carbonates of Group 1 compounds, e.g. K_2CO_3, Na_2CO_3.
- All nitrate compounds.
- Most common chloride compounds.
- Most common sulfate compounds.
- All alkalis, e.g. NaOH, $Ca(OH)_2$ (also known as slaked lime).

Solubility of Ionic Compounds (cont.)

The following are **insoluble** in water.
- Silver and lead halides, e.g. $AgCl$, $PbCl_2$.
- Sulfates of lead, barium and calcium, e.g. $BaSO_4$.
- Most common carbonate compounds, e.g. $CaCO_3$, $CuCO_3$.
- Most common hydroxide compounds, e.g. $Mg(OH)_2$ (also known as milk of magnesia).

Insoluble Salts

If the salt is formed by mixing two solutions is insoluble, it will form a solid **precipitate**. This is a **precipitation reaction**. For example:

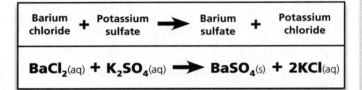

Barium chloride	+	Potassium sulfate	→	Barium sulfate	+	Potassium chloride

$$BaCl_2{(aq)} + K_2SO_4{(aq)} \rightarrow BaSO_4{(s)} + 2KCl{(aq)}$$

The pure solid salt can be separated by filtering the mixture, washing the solid residue in the filter paper with distilled water and drying the solid in a warm oven.

This can be demonstrated in the laboratory by mixing lead nitrate solution with sodium iodide solution.

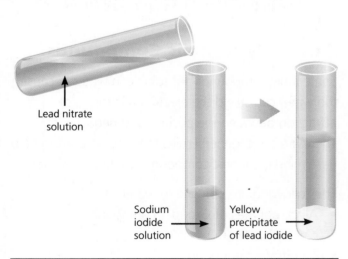

Lead nitrate solution

Sodium iodide solution

Yellow precipitate of lead iodide

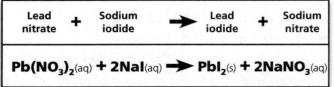

Lead nitrate	+	Sodium iodide	→	Lead iodide	+	Sodium nitrate

$$Pb(NO_3)_2{(aq)} + 2NaI{(aq)} \rightarrow PbI_2{(s)} + 2NaNO_3{(aq)}$$

The lead iodide mixture can then be filtered. The residue can then be washed with distilled water and dried.

Yellow lead iodide suspended in solution of sodium nitrate

Yellow lead iodide particles left behind on filter paper

Sodium nitrate solution

Dry yellow solid of lead iodide on filter paper

Remember that lead chloride and silver chloride are insoluble. The sulfates of barium, calcium and lead are also insoluble.

Barium Sulfate

Barium sulfate ($BaSO_4$) is extremely insoluble in water. This allows it to be used both in the laboratory and in medicine. In the laboratory it is the formation of barium sulfate that identifies sulfate ions in ionic substances.

In medicine, barium sulfate is used for barium meals, which are fed to X-ray patients. Soft tissue does not show up sufficiently well for diagnoses on plain X-rays. Barium sulfate is opaque to X-rays so helps soft tissues such as the digestive tract to become visible.

Barium salts in general are toxic if ingested. This is because they are soluble and can be absorbed by the body. In comparison, barium sulfate is considered non-toxic because it is highly insoluble and is not absorbed into the bloodstream.

Identifying Ions

An ionic substance can be identified by determining each type of **ion** within it. Each ion has its own unique test so this makes it easy to identify.

We can find out exactly what makes up a particular substance and subsequently determine whether or not the substance is harmful.

Test for Chloride Ions

To test for **chloride ions**, dilute nitric acid and silver nitrate solution are added to a solution of the ionic substance. If the ionic substance contains chloride ions then a white precipitate will be made.

| Silver nitrate solution | + | Chloride ions (Cl^-) | → | White precipitate |

For example:

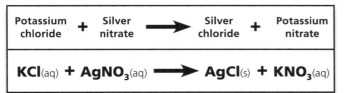

| Potassium chloride | + | Silver nitrate | → | Silver chloride | + | Potassium nitrate |

$$KCl_{(aq)} + AgNO_{3(aq)} \longrightarrow AgCl_{(s)} + KNO_{3(aq)}$$

Tests for Compound Ions

Compound ions are ions that contain atoms of more than one element. These ions can be identified.

Identifying Carbonate Ions (CO_3^{2-})

Carbonate ions are compound ions. Carbonates (CO_3^{2-}) react with dilute acids to produce carbon dioxide. Therefore, if the unknown substance is a carbonate, it releases carbon dioxide when dilute acid is added to it. The CO_2 can be identified by testing with limewater.

For example:

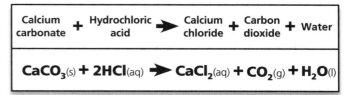

| Calcium carbonate | + | Hydrochloric acid | → | Calcium chloride | + | Carbon dioxide | + | Water |

$$CaCO_{3(s)} + 2HCl_{(aq)} \longrightarrow CaCl_{2(aq)} + CO_{2(g)} + H_2O_{(l)}$$

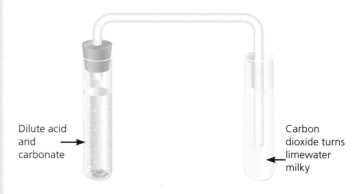

Dilute acid and carbonate →

Carbon dioxide turns limewater milky

Identifying Sulfate Ions (SO_4^{2-})

When dilute hydrochloric acid and barium chloride solution are added to SO_4^{2-} **ions**, a white precipitate forms.

Therefore, if dilute hydrochloric acid and barium chloride solution are added to a solution of the unknown substance and a white precipitate forms, the substance contains SO_4^{2-} ions:

| Sulfate ions | + | Barium ions | → | Barium sulfate (white precipitate) |

$$SO_4^{2-}{}_{(aq)} + Ba^{2+}{}_{(aq)} \longrightarrow BaSO_{4(s)} \text{ (white precipitate)}$$

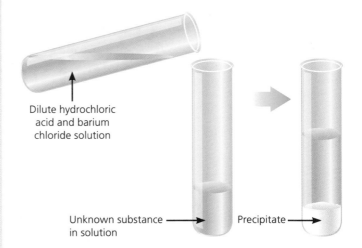

Dilute hydrochloric acid and barium chloride solution

Unknown substance in solution → Precipitate →

Using Flames to Identify Ions

When held in a Bunsen flame, compounds of different metals produce different flame colours:

- sodium (Na^+) = yellow flame
- potassium (K^+) = lilac flame
- calcium (Ca^{2+}) = brick-red flame
- copper (Cu^{2+}) = blue–green flame.

Therefore, metal ions can easily be identified by heating a paste of the unknown ionic substance in a hot (blue) Bunsen flame.

To carry out a flame test to test for these metal ions, a paste of the solid compound is made with a small amount of hydrochloric acid. The end of the flame test wire (a nichrome wire) is dipped in the paste and held in the Bunsen flame. If the flame glows with a colour that is associated with a particular metal, the ions of that metal must be present in the substance.

When Bunsen and Kirchhoff viewed a sodium flame through a spectroscope, they observed bright lines in the yellow part of the visible spectrum.

Using spectroscopy to view other metals in their compounds this way showed that each metal had a distinct fingerprint in the spectrum and led to the discovery of new elements, including rubidium and caesium.

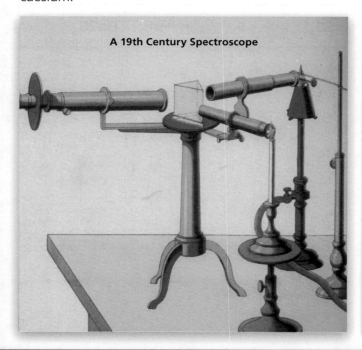

A 19th Century Spectroscope

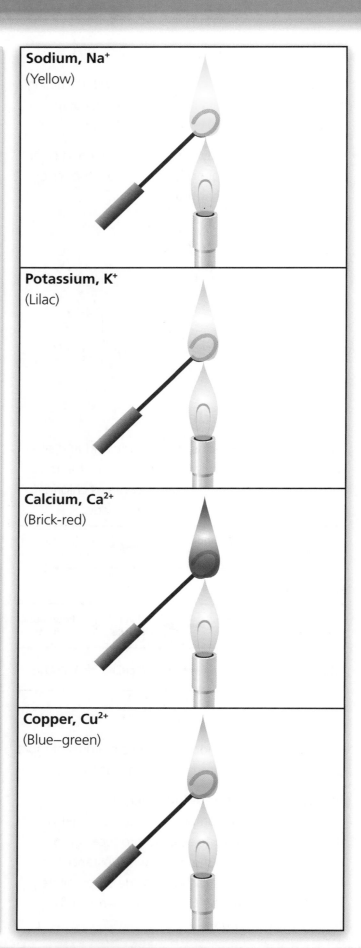

Sodium, Na⁺
(Yellow)

Potassium, K⁺
(Lilac)

Calcium, Ca²⁺
(Brick-red)

Copper, Cu²⁺
(Blue–green)

C2 Topic 3: Covalent Compounds and Separation Techniques

This topic looks at:

- how non-metals form molecules and compounds
- the properties of covalent compounds
- the properties and uses of diamond and graphite
- how immiscible and miscible liquids are separated
- what chromatography is and how it can be used

The Covalent Bond

A **covalent bond** occurs between non-metal atoms. The atoms share electrons in order to complete their outer shells. A covalent bond can occur between atoms of the same element or atoms of different elements. It results in the formation of **molecules**.

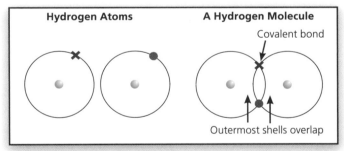

Hydrogen Atoms   **A Hydrogen Molecule**

Covalent bond

Outermost shells overlap

A **single covalent bond** is formed when two atoms share one pair of electrons. Each atom shares one electron in the bond, as in the example above – a hydrogen molecule.

If two pairs of electrons are shared, a **double bond** is formed. Each atom shares two of its electrons in the bond.

Examples

Hydrogen atoms and chlorine atoms can join together to form hydrogen chloride (HCl).

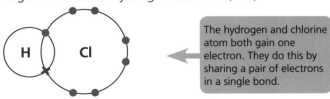

The hydrogen and chlorine atom both gain one electron. They do this by sharing a pair of electrons in a single bond.

Hydrogen atoms and oxygen atoms can join together to form water (H_2O).

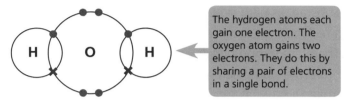

The hydrogen atoms each gain one electron. The oxygen atom gains two electrons. They do this by sharing a pair of electrons in a single bond.

Carbon atoms and hydrogen atoms can join together to form methane (CH_4).

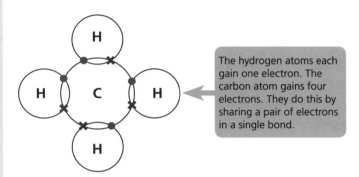

The hydrogen atoms each gain one electron. The carbon atom gains four electrons. They do this by sharing a pair of electrons in a single bond.

HT Both oxygen atoms achieve full outer shells by sharing electrons. They do this by sharing two pairs of electrons in a double covalent bond.

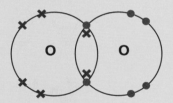

Carbon atoms and oxygen atoms can join together to form carbon dioxide (CO_2). The oxygen atoms each need two electrons to achieve a full outer shell. The carbon atom needs four electrons to achieve a full outer shell. They do this by sharing two pairs of electrons in a double covalent bond.

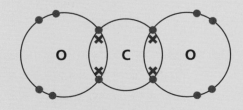

Properties of Simple Covalent Molecules

Substances with simple covalent structures consist of small molecules containing relatively few atoms. There are strong bonds between the atoms in the molecules, but there are weak forces between the molecules (weak inter-molecular forces).

This means that substances containing simple molecules have low melting and boiling points and have no overall charge so they cannot conduct electricity.

At room temperature many substances exist as gases, usually made up of molecules consisting of more than one atom. Again, there are strong covalent bonds within molecules but virtually no force of attraction between them. For example:

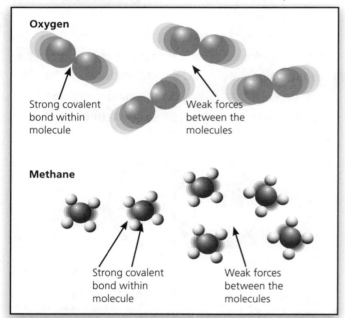

Covalent Structures – Giant Molecules

Giant covalent structures have many atoms joined to each other covalently throughout the whole structure. This makes their properties very different from those of simple covalently bonded molecules.

For example, each carbon atom in the Structures of diamond and graphite shares its electrons with the atom next to it. This gives diamond and graphite giant regular structures with high melting and boiling points.

Diamond (A Form of Carbon)

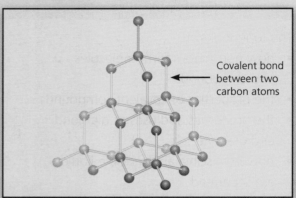

Diamond is a giant, rigid, covalent structure (lattice) in which each carbon atom forms four covalent bonds with other carbon atoms. The strength of the covalent bonds results in diamond having very high melting and boiling points, which makes diamond very hard but unable to conduct electricity. This makes diamond a useful substance for making cutting tools.

Graphite (A Form of Carbon)

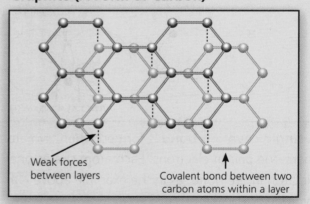

Graphite is a giant, covalent, layered structure. The layers can slide past each other, making graphite soft and slippery. Like diamond, graphite has high melting and boiling points. There are weak forces of attraction between layers because each carbon atom forms only three covalent bonds within the layers, so one electron from each carbon atom can be delocalised (moved). This allows graphite to conduct heat and electricity. Graphite is used to make electrodes and lubricants.

Testing Different Compounds

It is possible to demonstrate the differences in properties between some ionic and some covalent compounds by:

- trying to melt them, using a Bunsen burner
- placing electrodes into a sample of the substance to see if it conducts electricity as a solid, liquid or aqueous solution
- timing how long it takes the substance to dissolve in water.

You may have done these tests with sodium chloride, magnesium sulfate, sucrose (sugar) and some other compounds.

Separating Mixtures

Solids can form mixtures and if one of the solids is soluble in water then the mixture can easily be separated by filtration. Liquids can also be mixed together. They too can be separated.

When two liquids, such as oil and water, are mixed together and form distinct separate layers they are called **immiscible** (they cannot mix together). In this example, the water can be separated from the oil using a separating funnel as shown in the diagram opposite.

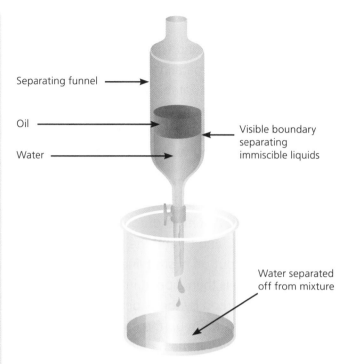

When liquids are mixed together and they stay mixed together they are called **miscible**. In this case the liquids have to be separated by a different method. They are separated using distillation or fractional distillation. For example, liquid air is a mixture of gases that have been cooled to a liquid and then separated by fractional distillation.

Fractional Distillation of Air

Dry air is made up of gases, including oxygen, nitrogen and carbon dioxide. Both oxygen and nitrogen can be obtained by separating them from liquid air by means of **fractional distillation**. We use oxygen in steel-making and nitrogen for freezing food quickly.

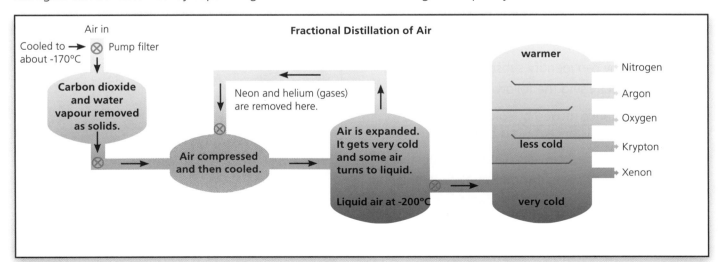

Chromatography

Evaporation, distillation and filtration are not always suitable methods for separating mixtures. For example, they are all unsuitable for separating the small amount of dissolved dyes used in food colourings. To separate such mixtures, a process called **chromatography** would have to be used.

Chromatography allows unknown components in a mixture to be identified by comparing them to known substances. A sample of four known substances (A, B, C and D) and the unknown substance (X) are put on a 'start line' on a piece of filter paper, which is then dipped into a solvent. As the solvent is absorbed by the paper it dissolves the samples and carries them up the paper. The substances will move up the paper at different rates because the different substances have different levels of solubility. The unknown substance (X) can be identified by comparing the horizontal spots.

The more soluble the substance is, then the further up the paper the substance is carried by the solvent. For paper chromatography this is usually water. Other solvents used in chromatography include ethanol.

Different methods of chromatography have been developed, resulting in a wide range of uses in the medical, chemical, food and forensics professions. Chromatography can be used to check foodstuffs for additives, contaminants and other substances. It can also be used by forensic investigators to separate traces of chemicals in house or building fires and to identify seized drugs.

Chromatography can identify substances by working out their R_f values using the following formula:

$$R_f \text{ value} = \frac{\text{distance moved by soluble substance}}{\text{distance moved by solvent}}$$

Once the R_f value has been calculated, the substance can be identified by comparison to published tables. An unknown amino acid in a food can easily be identified this way, or an unknown chemical found at the scene of a house fire.

Apparatus For Chromatography

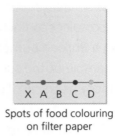

Spots of food colouring on filter paper

Solvent

By comparing food colourings A, B, C and D to substance X, we can see that substance X is food colouring D.

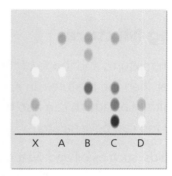

A chromatogram showing how the food colourings have split into their dyes

C2 Topic 4: Groups in the Periodic Table

This topic looks at:

- the structure and properties of metals
- the transition metals and their typical properties
- the alkali metals and their typical properties and reactions
- the halogens and their typical properties and reactions
- the noble gases, how they were discovered and their properties and uses
- how elements and compounds are classified and how their properties differ according to their structure

Metals

Metal atoms form giant crystalline structures. The atoms are packed tightly together so the outer electrons become separated from the atom. The result is a lattice structure of positive ions in a sea of free-moving electrons.

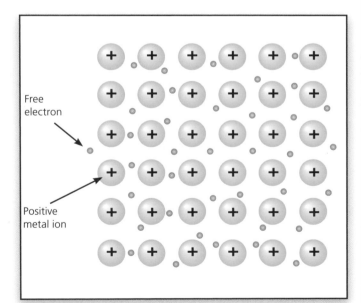

Free electron

Positive metal ion

Metals are very good conductors of electricity because their outer shell electrons can move freely within the structure, carrying the electric charge.

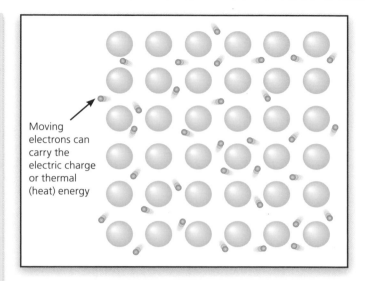

Moving electrons can carry the electric charge or thermal (heat) energy

Metal ions align in their structure in layers, which gives rise to their malleability. The layers can easily slide over each other.

The Transition Metals

The **transition metals** are included in the central block between Group 2 and Group 3 of the periodic table.

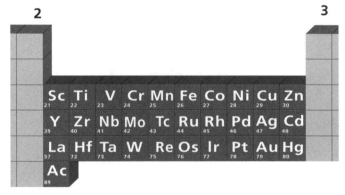

Iron and copper are well-known examples of transition elements.

Copper – A Transition Metal – Used to Make Pipes

Properties of the Transition Metals

- Transition metals are malleable, ductile and dense and have high melting points.
- They are good conductors of heat and electricity.
- Transition metal compounds are often coloured; for example, copper sulfate crystals are blue.

The Alkali Metals

The **alkali metals** occupy the first vertical group (Group 1) at the left-hand side of the periodic table. Lithium, sodium and potassium are typical members of this group.

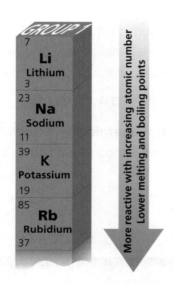

Properties of the Alkali Metals

- They are soft and have low melting points (e.g. potassium has a melting point of 63°C).
- Their reactions with water become increasingly exothermic (increase in temperature).
- Their high degree of reactivity means they must be stored under oil.
- The further down Group 1 the metal is, the greater its reactivity.
- The further down Group 1 the metal is, the further away the lone outer electron is from the nucleus.
- Francium is the most reactive alkali metal: its nucleus is unstable and it is a radioactive element.
- They react vigorously with water to form hydroxides, which are alkaline (higher than 7 on the pH scale), and hydrogen gas.

A simple test can be performed for hydrogen gas. Hydrogen collected in the inverted test tube makes a squeaky pop when lit.

Test tube of hydrogen — Pop! — Lighted splint

Reactions of the Alkali Metals

On contact with water, lithium floats, begins to move around and fizzes.

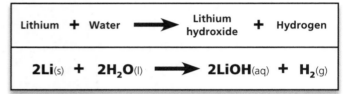

| Lithium | + | Water | → | Lithium hydroxide | + | Hydrogen |

$$2Li_{(s)} + 2H_2O_{(l)} \longrightarrow 2LiOH_{(aq)} + H_2{}_{(g)}$$

On contact with water, sodium shoots across the water surface and fizzes vigorously.

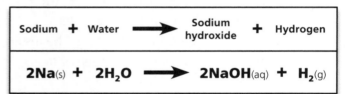

| Sodium | + | Water | → | Sodium hydroxide | + | Hydrogen |

$$2Na_{(s)} + 2H_2O \longrightarrow 2NaOH_{(aq)} + H_2{}_{(g)}$$

Potassium has a more violent reaction as the gas ignites whilst the metal moves very quickly across the surface of the water.

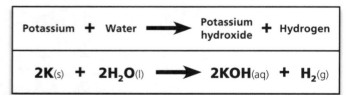

| Potassium | + | Water | → | Potassium hydroxide | + | Hydrogen |

$$2K_{(s)} + 2H_2O_{(l)} \longrightarrow 2KOH_{(aq)} + H_2{}_{(g)}$$

Reactivity of Group 1 Alkali Metals

Alkali metals react to lose their outer electron and gain a full outer shell. The smaller the atom, the greater the effect of the attractive force of the protons in the nucleus, so the lone outer electron is held in place. As the atoms get bigger this effect decreases. The outer electron is lost more easily and the metal is therefore more reactive.

Halogens

The **halogens** are found in Group 7 of the periodic table. There are five non-metals in Group 7; the top four are the ones you need to remember. They are all different in colour. Their melting and boiling points determine their physical state at room temperature. The halogens all exist as diatomic molecules.

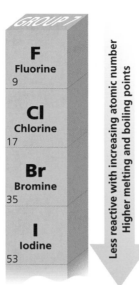

Halogen	Fluorine	Chlorine	Bromine	Iodine
Boiling Point (°C)	-188°C	-34°C	59°C (melting point -7°C)	187°C (melting point 114°C)
Colour and Physical State at Room Temperature	Pale yellow gas	Pale green gas	Red-brown liquid	Dark grey solid

Displacement Reactions

The halogens' atomic numbers increase as we go down the group and they become less reactive. This can be shown by the **displacement reactions** of halogens with solutions of other **halides**. In summary:

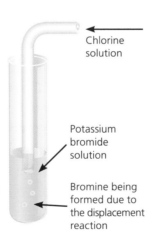

Chlorine solution

Potassium bromide solution

Bromine being formed due to the displacement reaction

- fluorine is the most reactive, followed by chlorine
- bromine and iodine are the least reactive.

	Potassium Chloride	Potassium Bromide	Potassium Iodide
Fluorine F_2	Potassium fluoride and chlorine	Potassium fluoride and bromine	Potassium fluoride and iodine
Chlorine Cl_2	✕	Potassium chloride and bromine	Potassium chloride and iodine
Bromine Br_2	No reaction	✕	Potassium bromide and iodine
Iodine I_2	No reaction	No reaction	✕

If there is a displacement reaction then it will follow this pattern.

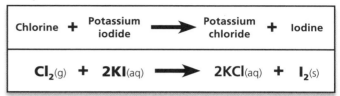

$$Cl_{2(g)} + 2KI_{(aq)} \longrightarrow 2KCl_{(aq)} + I_{2(s)}$$

Uses of the Halogens

Chlorine is used to kill bacteria, for example, in swimming pools and domestic water supplies. It is also used for bleaching paper, wood and cloth. Iodine solution is used as an antiseptic.

Reactions of Halogens and Iron

Iron, in the form of iron wool, is heated strongly and **chlorine** gas is passed over it in a fume cupboard. The iron wool will glow brightly as the following reaction takes place.

Glowing iron wool

Chlorine gas in

Chlorine gas out

Heat

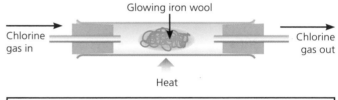

$$2Fe_{(s)} + 3Cl_{2(g)} \longrightarrow 2FeCl_{3(s)}$$

Chlorine will react with other metals to form chlorides. For example:

$$2Na_{(s)} + Cl_{2(g)} \longrightarrow 2NaCl_{(s)}$$

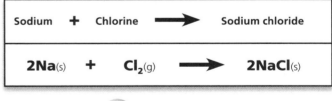

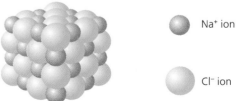

Na⁺ ion

Cl⁻ ion

So, one atom of sodium plus one atom of chlorine produces sodium chloride. Bromine will form bromides and iodine will form iodides.

Reactions of Halogens with Hydrogen

The halogens will react with hydrogen to give hydrogen halides.

Hydrogen halides will form colourless acidic gases which are highly soluble in water. The resultant solution is acidic. For example:

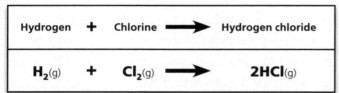

Then dissolve this gas in water.

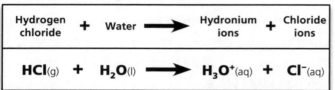

Discovery of Noble Gases

In the late 1880s Sir William Ramsey recorded a visible spectrum for an unknown gas that matched and confirmed the earlier discovery of **helium**.

Argon was discovered in 1895 when Rayleigh and Ramsey measured the densities of gases and compared nitrogen obtained from ammonia to nitrogen left when other gases were removed from air. A visible spectrum told them that this was a previously unknown gas, which they named argon.

Neon was discovered in 1898 when Ramsey and Morris Travers discovered other lines in the visible spectrum for argon.

Again, visible spectra were used to identify **krypton**, when known constituents were boiled off from a sample of air.

Xenon was found when it glowed bright blue in a discharge tube.

Scientists and chemists were able to use patterns in the physical properties of the noble gases, such as boiling point or density, to estimate values for other members of the group.

The Noble Gases

The **noble gases** are located in a vertical group at the right-hand side of the periodic table. This is called Group 0. The noble gases have no smell and are colourless. They glow with a particular colour when electricity passes through them. The noble gases generally do not react due to their full outer electron shell (a complete electronic arrangement). (Note that helium has two electrons in its outer shell.)

All the elements in Group 0 are **chemically inert**, which means they are unreactive.

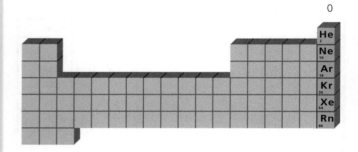

Uses of the Noble Gases

- Helium is used in airships and weather balloons because it is much less dense than air and is non-flammable.
- Argon is used in light bulbs because it is unreactive and provides an inert atmosphere.
- Argon is also used in welding, where it acts like a shield around the weld until the metal cools, preventing any reaction with oxygen in the air.
- Argon, krypton and neon are all used in fluorescent lights and discharge tubes.

Summary of the Different Types of Structure and Bonding

Ionic Compounds

There are millions of different substances in existence. Some compounds are made up of ions. These substances are all solids at room temperature. The ions can be positively charged (metals and hydrogen) or negatively charged (non-metals). The oppositely charged ions will be attracted by a strong electrostatic attraction, which is known as an ionic bond. It is the strong attractive forces between the oppositely charged ions that give the ionic compounds many of their properties.

Molecular Compounds

Some substances are made up of molecules. These molecules are said to have a simple or small molecule structure and contain atoms that are joined together by covalent bonds. This type of bond involves the sharing of pairs of electrons between non-metal atoms.

The covalent bonds between the atoms within the molecules are very strong. There are no bonds between the molecules but the molecules are held in their structure by weak attractive forces between them, called intermolecular forces.

It is these weak intermolecular forces between the molecules that give rise to their low boiling and melting points and whether they are a solid, liquid or gas at room temperature.

Giant Covalent Structures

As well as forming small molecules, non-metal atoms can also form giant covalent structures in which all the atoms are joined together by covalent bonds in a massive network. The covalent bonds that keep these atoms together within their structure are (like these bonds in small molecules) very strong and give the substances their properties.

Metallic Structures

About three-quarters of the elements in the periodic table are metals. Metal atoms form a giant, regular structure held together by the strong electrostatic attractions of positive metal ions and the free-moving outer shell electrons. This metallic structure gives metals their chemical properties.

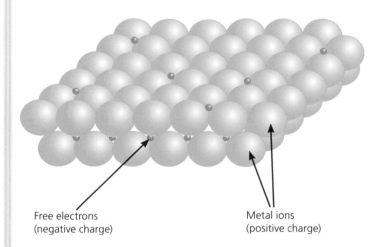

Free electrons
(negative charge)

Metal ions
(positive charge)

Each of these types of bonding and their resultant properties can be compared in the table below.

Bonding	Ionic (between metals and non-metals)	Covalent (between non-metals)		Metallic (between metals)
Structure	Giant ionic	Giant covalent	Simple molecular	Giant metallic
Melting and Boiling Point	High	High	Low	High
Soluble in Water	Yes	No	Yes	No
Conduct Electricity	As a solid, no; when molten or in solution, yes (ions are free to move)	No	No	Yes (free electrons)

Energy Changes in Chemical Reactions

A **chemical reaction** involves two or more **reactants** reacting together to make new substances, known as **products**. Reactants and products may be elements or compounds.

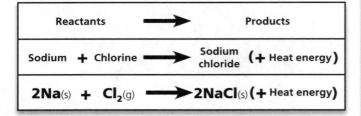

Temperature Changes in Reactions

All chemical reactions are accompanied by a temperature change.

Exothermic reactions are accompanied by a rise in temperature. Thermal (heat) energy is transferred out to the surroundings. Combustion is an example of an exothermic reaction.

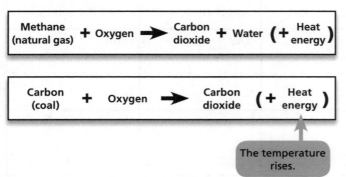

The temperature rises.

Other exothermic reactions include:
- respiration in body cells
- hydration of ethene to form ethanol
- neutralising alkalis with acids.

Endothermic reactions and changes are accompanied by a fall in temperature. Thermal energy is transferred in from the surroundings. Dissolving ammonium nitrate crystals in water is an example of an endothermic change.

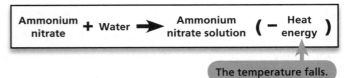

The temperature falls.

Examples of endothermic reactions include:
- the reaction between citric acid and sodium hydrogencarbonate solution
- polymerisation of ethene to polyethene
- reduction of silver ions to silver in photography.

By carrying out some chemical reactions and measuring the temperature before and after, it is possible to see that chemical reactions can be endothermic or exothermic. For example:
- dissolving ethanoic acid in sodium carbonate is accompanied by a temperature drop
- reacting sodium hydroxide with hydrochloric acid is accompanied by a temperature rise
- displacing copper from a solution of copper sulfate, using zinc powder, is accompanied by a temperature rise.

Making and Breaking Bonds

Energy must be supplied to break chemical bonds.

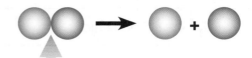

Energy in (Endothermic)

Energy is released when chemical bonds are made.

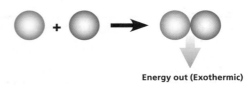

Energy out (Exothermic)

In order to produce new substances in a chemical reaction, the bonds in the reactants must be broken and new bonds must be made in the products.

If more energy is needed to break old bonds than is released when new bonds are made, the reaction is endothermic overall.

If more energy is released when new bonds are made than is needed to break the old bonds, the reaction is exothermic overall.

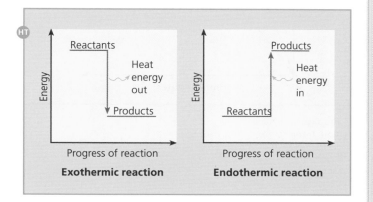

Exothermic reaction   **Endothermic reaction**

Rates of Reaction

Chemical reactions happen at different rates (for example, within seconds, days or even years).

Rates of chemical reactions can be increased so that the reactions take place more quickly. This can be achieved by:
- increasing the **temperature** of the reactants so the particles collide more frequently
- increasing the **surface area** of the solid reactants so the particles collide more frequently
- increasing the **concentration** of one of the reactants so the particles collide more frequently.

Collision Theory

Chemical reactions usually occur when reacting particles collide with each other with sufficient energy to react.

All substances are made up of particles. These particles may be atoms, molecules or ions. In a chemical reaction these reactant particles collide with each other. Not all chemical reactions work because the particles, on colliding, may rebound and remain unchanged if they do not posses sufficient energy to break bonds.

Low Temperature
In a cold reaction mixture the particles are moving quite slowly – the particles collide with each other less often, with less energy, and fewer collisions are successful in a given time (per second).

High Temperature
If we heat the reaction mixture, the particles move more quickly – the particles collide with each other more often, with greater energy, and many more collisions are successful in a given time (per second).

Small Surface Area
Large particles have a small surface area in relation to their volume – fewer particles are exposed and available for collisions. This results in fewer collisions per second and a slower reaction.

Large Surface Area
Small particles have a large surface area in relation to their volume – more particles are exposed and available for collisions. This results in more collisions per second and a faster reaction.

Low Concentration
In a reaction where one or both reactants are in low concentrations, the particles are spread out and collide with each other less often, resulting in fewer successful collisions per second.

High Concentration
In a reaction where one or both reactants are in high concentrations, the particles are packed closely together and collide with each other more often, resulting in more successful collisions per second.

Examples of Changing Rates of Reactions

Calcium carbonate reacts with hydrochloric acid to produce calcium chloride, water and carbon dioxide.

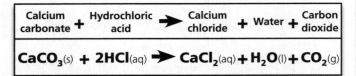

| Calcium carbonate | + | Hydrochloric acid | → | Calcium chloride | + | Water | + | Carbon dioxide |

$$CaCO_3{}_{(s)} + 2HCl_{(aq)} \rightarrow CaCl_2{}_{(aq)} + H_2O_{(l)} + CO_2{}_{(g)}$$

We can measure how long it takes a given mass of calcium carbonate to react completely and see how changing factors can affect the rate of the reaction.

1 Heating the solution makes the reaction occur more quickly.

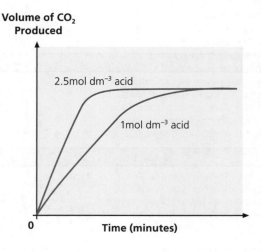

Volume of CO$_2$ Produced

45°C

30°C

Time (minutes)

2 Increasing the concentration of the acid makes the reaction occur more quickly.

Volume of CO$_2$ Produced

2.5mol dm^{-3} acid

1mol dm^{-3} acid

Time (minutes)

3 Making the solid have a large surface area increases the rate of the reaction. This can be seen by measuring the amount of carbon dioxide given off every minute. Calcium carbonate chips and then the same mass of finely crushed calcium carbonate can be used.

N.B. There is the same mass of calcium carbonate in both reactions, so the same volume of carbon dioxide is produced.

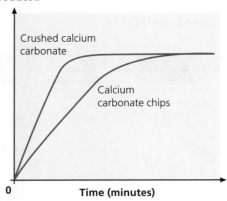

Volume of CO$_2$ Produced

Crushed calcium carbonate

Calcium carbonate chips

Time (minutes)

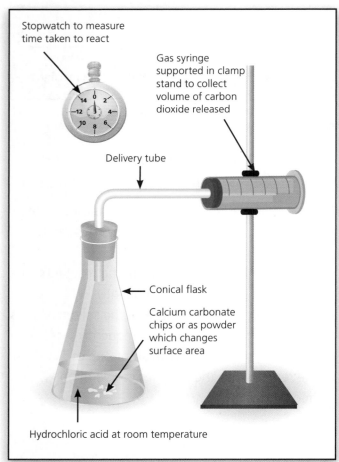

Stopwatch to measure time taken to react

Gas syringe supported in clamp stand to collect volume of carbon dioxide released

Delivery tube

Conical flask

Calcium carbonate chips or as powder which changes surface area

Hydrochloric acid at room temperature

Catalysts

A **catalyst** is a substance that increases the rate of a chemical reaction, without being used up in the process. Catalysts are often specific: different reactions require different catalysts. Because catalysts are not used up, only small amounts of them are needed.

Catalysts work by reducing the minimum energy needed for a chemical reaction to happen.

Since catalysts lower the amount of energy needed for successful collisions, higher numbers of particles will have enough energy so there will be more successful collisions per second and the reaction will be faster. Also, they can provide a surface for the molecules to attach to, thereby increasing the chances of molecules bumping into each other.

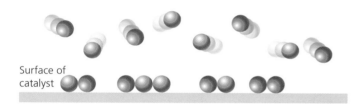

Surface of catalyst

Below is a graph showing the decomposition of hydrogen peroxide to water, where the rate of reaction is measured by the amount of oxygen given off at one-minute intervals. The reaction is shown with and without a catalyst. As the graph shows, the reaction happens very slowly, unless a catalyst is added.

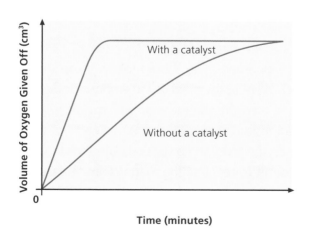

Volume of Oxygen Given Off (cm³)

With a catalyst

Without a catalyst

0

Time (minutes)

Catalytic Converters in Cars

A catalytic converter will change pollutant gases in car exhaust fumes into less harmful gases.

A catalytic converter contains a honeycomb filter where each individual cell is coated with catalysing metals, usually a mixture of platinum and rhodium. This structure increases the surface area of the converter, which increases the rate of conversion of the gas carbon monoxide into carbon dioxide.

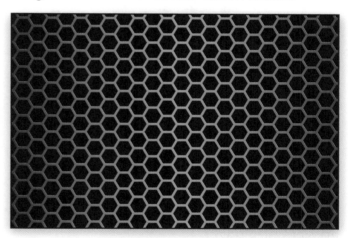

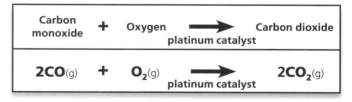

Carbon monoxide	+	Oxygen	$\longrightarrow$ platinum catalyst	Carbon dioxide
$2CO_{(g)}$	+	$O_{2(g)}$	$\longrightarrow$ platinum catalyst	$2CO_{2(g)}$

The catalytic converter also helps to oxidise unburned fuel to produce carbon dioxide and water. To help convert the gases the catalytic converter works best at a higher temperature. Increasing the temperature will also have the effect of increasing the rate of conversion of the gases.

C2 | Quantitative Chemistry

C2 Topic 6: Quantitative Chemistry

This topic looks at:
- how different types of calculations are used
- how balanced equations are used in reacting mass calculations
- what chemical yields are
- how industry uses chemical reactions

Relative Formula Mass

The **relative formula mass** of a compound is the sum of the relative atomic masses of all its elements added together. To calculate it, we need to know the formula of the compound and the relative atomic masses of all the atoms involved.

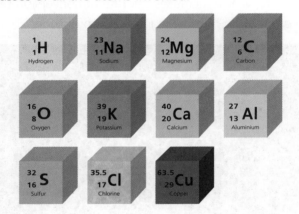

Example 1

Using the data above, calculate the relative formula mass of water, H_2O.

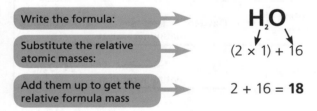

Write the formula: → H_2O

Substitute the relative atomic masses: → $(2 \times 1) + 16$

Add them up to get the relative formula mass → $2 + 16 = \textbf{18}$

Example 2

Using the data above, calculate the relative formula mass of potassium carbonate, K_2CO_3.

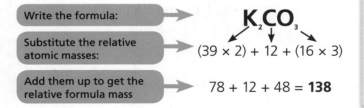

Write the formula: → K_2CO_3

Substitute the relative atomic masses: → $(39 \times 2) + 12 + (16 \times 3)$

Add them up to get the relative formula mass → $78 + 12 + 48 = \textbf{138}$

Empirical Formula

An **empirical formula** is the simplest whole-number formula that represents the ratio of atoms in a compound. There is one simple rule: **always divide the data you are given by the relative atomic mass of the element**. Then simplify the ratio to give you the simplest formula.

Example

Find the empirical formula of an oxide of iron, produced by reacting 1.12g of iron with 0.48g of oxygen. (Relative atomic masses: Fe = 56; O = 16)

> Identify the mass of the elements in the compound:

Masses: Fe = 1.12, O = 0.48

> Divide these masses by their relative atomic masses:

$Fe = \frac{1.12}{56} = 0.02$ $O = \frac{0.48}{16} = 0.03$

> Identify the ratio of atoms in the compound and simplify it:

Ratio = 0.02 : 0.03 → $\times 100$ 0.02 : 0.03 $\times 100$ 2 : 3

Empirical formula = $\textbf{Fe}_2\textbf{O}_3$

It is also possible to find the formula of magnesium oxide from an experiment.

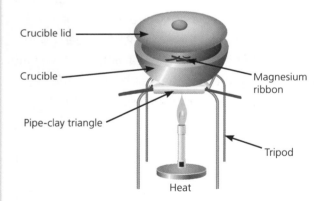

In this experiment, you should follow these steps.
1. First measure the mass of the empty crucible and lid.
2. Then measure the mass of the crucible with the magnesium inside.
3. Once the crucible has been heated for long enough to react all the magnesium, measure the final mass.
4. From the mass measurements, work out the empirical formula.

Percentage Composition by Mass

Using the relative formula mass you can determine the percentage composition by mass of a compound.

$$\text{Percentage Composition by Mass of Element} = \frac{\text{RAM of Element}}{\text{RFM of Compound}} \times 100$$

Example 1

Find the percentage composition by mass of carbon in calcium carbonate, $CaCO_3$.
(Relative atomic masses: Ca = 40; C = 12; O = 16)

1. First, work out the relative formula mass of $CaCO_3$.

$$CaCO_3$$
$$40 + 12 + (16 \times 3) = 100$$

2. Substitute the relative masses of carbon and calcium carbonate into the formula:

$$\% \ C = \frac{\text{RAM of C}}{\text{RFM of CaCO}_3} \times 100 = \frac{12}{100} \times 100 = 12\%$$

Example 2

Find the percentage composition by mass of copper in copper sulfate, $CuSO_4$.
(Relative atomic masses: Cu = 63.5; S = 32; O = 16)

1. Relative formula mass of $CuSO_4$ =
   $63.5 + 32 + (16 \times 4) = 159.5$

2. Substituting the relative masses of Cu and $CuSO_4$ into the formula:

$$\% \ Cu = \frac{63.5}{159.5} \times 100 = \mathbf{39.8\%}$$

ⓗ Reacting Masses

All reactions follow the **law of conservation of mass**, which states that mass can neither be created nor destroyed. Therefore:

Total Mass of Reactants	=	Total Mass of Products

Total Mass of Reactants   Total Mass of Products

The law of conservation of mass can be used to work out how much reactant you need in a reaction, or how much product you will get from a reaction.

Calculating the Mass of a Product and a Reactant

Sometimes, we need to be able to work out how much of a substance is used up or produced in a chemical reaction.

Example 1

How much calcium oxide can be produced from 50kg of calcium carbonate? (Relative atomic masses: Ca = 40; C = 12; O = 16)

> Write down the equation:

$$CaCO_3 \longrightarrow CaO + CO_2$$

> Work out the relative formula mass of each substance:

$$40 + 12 + (3 \times 16) \longrightarrow (40 + 16) + [12 + (2 \times 16)]$$

> Check the total mass of reactants equals the total mass of the products. If they are not the same, check your work:

$$100 \longrightarrow 56 + 44 \ ✔$$

> Since the question only mentions calcium oxide and calcium carbonate, you can now ignore the carbon dioxide. You just need the ratio of mass of $CaCO_3$ to mass of CaO.

If 100kg of $CaCO_3$ produces 56kg of CaO, then 50kg of $CaCO_3$ produces $\frac{56}{2}$ kg of CaO = **28kg** of CaO.

Calculating the Mass of a Product and a Reactant (cont.)

Example 2

How much aluminium oxide (Al_2O_3) is needed to produce 540kg of aluminium?

(Relative atomic masses: Al = 27; O = 16)

Equation:

$$2Al_2O_3{(l)} \longrightarrow 4Al{(l)} + 3O_2{(g)}$$

Masses:

$$2[(27 \times 2) + (16 \times 3)] \longrightarrow (27 \times 4) + [3 \times (16 \times 2)]$$

$$Reactants \longrightarrow Products:$$

$$204 \longrightarrow 108 + 96$$

For this example we only need to look at Al_2O_3 and Al.

204kg of aluminium oxide (Al_2O_3) produces 108kg of aluminium (Al), so:

$\frac{204}{108}$ kg of Al_2O_3 will produce 1kg of Al

1.89kg of Al_2O_3 will produce 1kg of Al

But we want 540kg of Al.

Therefore, the amount of Al_2O_3 needed to produce 540kg of Al is:

540 × 1.89kg = **1021kg of Al_2O_3**

Example 3

The equation for the reaction between iron and sulfur is:

$$Fe{(s)} + S{(s)} \longrightarrow FeS{(s)}$$

When 14g of iron is heated with excess sulfur, how much iron(II) sulfide is formed?

(Relative atomic masses: Fe = 56; S = 32)

Formula mass of FeS = 56 + 32 = 88g

From the equation, 1 atom of Fe gives 1 formula of FeS, so:

56g of Fe give 88g of FeS

1g of Fe gives $\frac{88}{56}$g of FeS

So, 14g of Fe gives 14 × $\frac{88}{56}$g of FeS

= **22g** of FeS

Example 4

The reaction between magnesium and oxygen is:

$$2Mg{(s)} + O_2{(g)} \longrightarrow 2MgO{(s)}$$

How many grams of oxygen will react with 44g of magnesium?

(Relative atomic masses: Mg = 24; O = 16)

Formula mass of O_2 = 16 × 2 = 32g

From the equation, 2 atoms of Mg react with 1 formula (molecule) of O_2.

2 × 24g of Mg reacts with 32g of O_2

48g of Mg reacts with 32g of O_2

So, 1g of Mg reacts with $\frac{32}{48}$g of O_2

Therefore 44g of Mg reacts with 44 × $\frac{32}{48}$g of O_2

= **29.3g** of O_2

Product Yields

Chemical reactions often produce more than one **product**, and not all of these products are 'useful'. This means that not all of the starting materials (**reactants**) are converted into useful products. In a chemical reaction the amount of the useful product is known as the **yield**. The actual yield obtained from a chemical reaction is usually less than the expected yield.

The **expected or theoretical yield** is the amount of product expected from a reaction, based on the amount of reactants. Companies like to get the highest possible yield from the reaction, for the lowest cost. There are therefore two yields in a reaction:

- **theoretical yield** – calculated from the relative formula masses of reactants and products
- **actual yield** – the actual mass of useful product obtained from the reaction in the experiment.

From comparing these two yields, we can calculate the percentage yield:

$$\text{Percentage yield} = \frac{\text{Actual yield}}{\text{Theoretical yield}} \times 100\%$$

Example

In a chemical reaction 360g of silver nitrate, $AgNO_3$, was reacted with excess magnesium chloride, $MgCl_2$, and found to produce 264g of silver chloride, AgCl.

Calculate the percentage yield of this reaction.

(Relative atomic masses: Ag = 108; Cl = 35.5; N = 14; O = 16)

1 Write down the equation of the reaction.

Silver nitrate	+	Magnesium chloride	→	Silver chloride	+	Magnesium nitrate

$$2AgNO_{3\,(aq)} + MgCl_{2(aq)} \rightarrow 2AgCl_{(s)} + Mg(NO_3)_{2(aq)}$$

N.B. This must be the balanced equation for the reaction. You can make sure it is correct by checking that the mass of the reactants is equal to the mass of the products.

2 Work out the relative formula masses for $AgNO_3$ and AgCl using the relative atomic masses given.

$AgNO_3 = 108 + 14 + (16 \times 3) = 170$

$AgCl = 108 + 35.5 = 143.5$

3 The formula mass of $AgNO_3 = 170g$

So, 360g of $AgNO_3 = \frac{360}{170} = 2.12$ formulas

4 From the equation of the reaction, 2 formulas of $AgNO_3$ produces 2 formulas of AgCl, so the ratio is 1 : 1.

Therefore 2.12 formulas of $AgNO_3$ produces 2.12 formulas of AgCl.

The mass of AgCl that this represents is $2.12 \times 143.5 = 304.22g$ of AgCl.

So, the theoretical yield for the reaction is 304.22g AgCl.

5 Actual yield obtained was 264g of AgCl.

So, percentage yield $= \frac{264}{304.22} \times 100 = \textbf{86.8\%}$.

From the example shown above, the percentage yield was not 100%, which is what an industrial process aims for. There are several factors involved in the yield of a chemical reaction:

- Chemical reactions may not be completed in the time available.
- Product may be lost during the purification procedure.
- Other reactions may be happening at the same time as the main reaction.

Not all chemical reactions produce only one product. Most produce waste. In the previous example only silver chloride was the useful product. The magnesium nitrate would have been wasted and disposed of because there was no commercial use for the material. For the company this can result in:

- an increase in process cost in order to dispose of the waste safely
- an increase in environmental concerns associated with the disposal method, as this could lead to air, water or land pollution.

Economics and the Chemical Industry

In the chemical industry chemists are constantly working to find the economically most favourable reactions. They are looking for the following key points:

- High percentage yield – a low yield will mean that more useful product would need to be produced from additional reactions.
- All products are commercially useful – if the reaction used for a particular process produces substances that have no use, then those particular products need to be disposed of, which costs money.
- Reactions occur at a suitable speed – a chemical reaction that is too slow would result in an expensive product, but a reaction that is too fast reaction could be potentially dangerous.

For example, in the Haber process, which produces ammonia on a large scale, it is important to get the maximum yield in the shortest possible time:

- A **low temperature** increases the yield of ammonia but the reaction is too slow.
- A **high pressure** increases the yield of ammonia but the process is too expensive.
- A **catalyst** increases the rate at which equilibrium is reached but does not affect the yield of ammonia.

Any hydrogen and nitrogen gas that remains unreacted is recycled back into the main reaction vessel. The heat generated as a result of the reaction is used to heat the catalyst and the process.

Questions labelled with an asterisk (*) are ones where the quality of your written communication will be assessed – you should take particular care with your spelling, punctuation and grammar, as well as the clarity of expression, on these questions.

1 **(a)** What type of structure do metal atoms form? **(1)**

(b) What do metal structures contain that allow them to conduct electricity and heat easily? **(1)**

(c) Transition metals have properties of typical metals. List three properties you would expect a transition metal to have. **(3)**

2 **(a)** Describe the difference between theoretical yield and actual yield. **(2)**

(b) Why is it important to obtain as high a yield as possible? **(1)**

(c) The equation shows the reaction for the decomposition of zinc carbonate when it is heated.

$$ZnCO_3{(s)} \longrightarrow ZnO{(s)} + CO_2{(g)}$$

(Relative atomic masses: Zn = 65; O = 16; C = 12)

(i) In an experiment 50.0g of zinc carbonate produced 31.5g of zinc oxide. The theoretical yield of zinc oxide for this reaction is 32.4g. Calculate the percentage yield. **(1)**

(ii) Calculate the percentage composition by mass of zinc in zinc oxide. **(2)**

(iii) What mass of zinc is in the 31.5g of zinc oxide formed in the experiment? **(1)**

3 **(a)** How would you show that the chemical reaction between sodium and chlorine is exothermic? **(1)**

(b) Describe how the energy involved in making and breaking bonds accounts for this type of reaction. **(3)**

(c) Which element will bromine displace, chlorine or iodine from solutions of their salts? Explain your answer. **(2)**

4 Describe why helium is used in airships and weather balloons. **(1)**

5 *Iodine has a simple molecular structure. Describe in as much detail as you can the type of bonding and resultant properties shown by iodine. **(6)**

6 Use the information below to answer the following questions.

Mass number
↓
$^{24}_{12}Mg$ $^{14}_{7}N$ $^{32}_{16}S$
↑
Atomic number

(a) In each of these elements, describe how the number of protons would be determined. **(1)**

(b) What is the number of electrons in each element? **(3)**

(c) How is the number of neutrons in each element calculated? **(1)**

(d) Using this information, draw the electronic configuration for each element. **(3)**

7 **(a)** State three ways in which a rate of chemical reaction can be changed. **(3)**

(b) What effect does increasing the frequency of collisions does what to a rate of reaction? **(1)**

(c) Why does a low concentration of particles result in a slower rate of reaction? **(2)**

(d) Describe an experiment to show how changing the surface area of calcium carbonate when it is reacted with hydrochloric acid can produce a change in the rate of reaction. **(4)**

(e) How does using a catalyst affect a rate of chemical reaction? **(3)**

8 (a) Ionic bonds are formed between which two types of atom?

A ☐ metal atom and metal atom

B ☐ metal atom and noble gas

C ☐ metal atom and non-metal atom

D ☐ non-metal atom and non-metal atom **(1)**

(b) An ionic bond involves

A ☐ sharing of electrons.

B ☐ transfer of protons.

C ☐ transfer of electrons.

D ☐ sharing of protons. **(1)**

(c) Predict the formula of the following ionic compounds:

(i) Barium chloride (Ba^{2+}, Cl^-) **(1)**

(ii) Magnesium oxide (Mg^{2+}, O^{2-}) **(1)**

(iii) Aluminium chloride (Al^{3+}, Cl^-) **(1)**

(iv) Iron oxide (Fe^{3+}, O^{2-}) **(1)**

HT 9 (a) Write the balanced symbol equation for the following reaction. **(2)**

Magnesium + Chlorine ⟶ Magnesium chloride

(b) Write the balanced symbol equation for the following reaction. **(2)**

Iron + Oxygen ⟶ Iron(III) oxide

10 Iron is made when aluminium reacts with iron oxide. This reaction can be shown by the following balanced symbol equation.

$$Fe_2O_3(s) + 2Al(s) \longrightarrow 2Fe(s) + Al_2O_3(s)$$

(Relative atomic masses: Fe = 56; Al = 27; O = 16)

(a) Work out the relative formula mass of each of the following:

(i) Fe_2O_3 (ii) Al_2O_3 **(2)**

(b) (i) What is the mass of aluminium needed to react with 800g of iron(III) oxide? **(3)**

(ii) What mass of iron is produced from 480g of iron(III) oxide? **(3)**

(iii) How much aluminium will be needed if 612g of aluminium oxide is produced? **(3)**

11 Diamond and graphite are two different forms of carbon. Describe the structure and properties of:

(a) diamond **(3)**

(b) graphite. **(3)**

P2 Topic 1: Static and Current Electricity

This topic looks at:
- how static charges arise
- everyday uses and dangers of static charges
- what an electric current is

The Atom

Atoms are basic particles from which all matter is made up.

Each atom has a small nucleus consisting of **protons** (positively charged) and **neutrons** (neutral). The nucleus is surrounded by **electrons** (negatively charged).

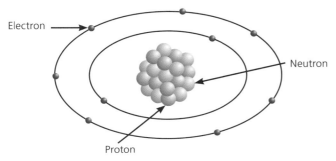

The proton and neutron have about the same mass as each other, but the electron is tiny in comparison. The mass of the electron is about one two-thousandth ($\frac{1}{2000}$) of the mass of a proton or neutron.

Static Electricity

Materials that allow electricity to flow through them easily are called **electrical conductors**. Metals are good electrical conductors. Plastics and many other materials, on the other hand, do not allow electricity to flow through them; they are called **insulators**.

However, it is possible for an insulator to become electrically charged if there is friction between it and another insulator. When this happens, electrons are transferred from one material to the other.
The insulator is then charged with **static electricity**. It is called 'static' because the electricity stays on the material and does not move.

You can generate static electricity by rubbing a balloon against your jumper. The electrically charged balloon will then attract very small objects.

Electric charge (static) builds up when electrons (which have a negative charge) are rubbed off one material on to another. The material **receiving electrons** becomes **negatively charged** and the material **giving up electrons** becomes **positively charged**. The charges transferred are equal and opposite.

For example, if you rub a Perspex rod with a cloth, it loses electrons to become positively charged. The cloth gains electrons to become negatively charged.

If you rub an ebonite rod with a piece of fur, it gains electrons to become negatively charged. The fur loses electrons to become positively charged.

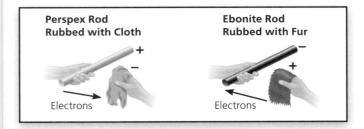

Repulsion and Attraction

When two charged materials are brought together, they exert a force on each other so they are **attracted** or **repelled**. Two materials with the **same type of charge repel each other**; two materials **with different types of charge attract each other**.

If you move a charged ebonite rod near to a suspended charged Perspex rod, the suspended Perspex rod will be attracted.

If you move a second charged Perspex rod near to the suspended charged Perspex rod, the suspended Perspex rod will be repelled.

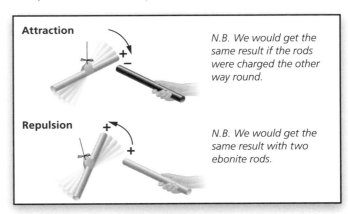

Common Electrostatic Phenomena

The following all involve the movement of electrons.

1. Lightning: clouds become charged up by rising hot air until discharge occurs, i.e. a bolt of lightning.
2. Charges on synthetic fabrics: static sparks when synthetic clothing is removed from the body.
3. Shocks from car doors: a car can become charged up due to friction between itself and air when it moves.
4. A negatively charged balloon brought near to a wall causes negative charges (electrons) to move away from the surface of the wall. This leaves the surface of the wall positively charged so the balloon and wall attract each other. A charged plastic comb will pick up small pieces of paper for the same reason.

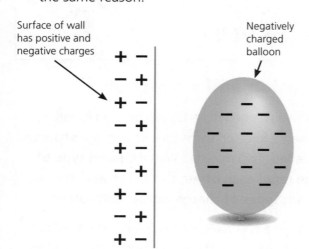

Surface of wall has positive and negative charges

Negatively charged balloon

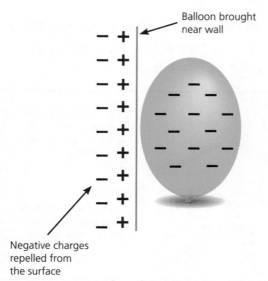

Balloon brought near wall

Negative charges repelled from the surface

Using Static in Everyday Life

The Laser Printer

An image of the page to be copied is projected onto an electrically charged plate (usually positively charged).

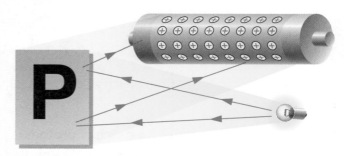

Light causes charge to leak away, leaving an electrostatic impression of the page.

This charged impression on the plate attracts tiny specks of oppositely charged black powder, which are then transferred from the plate to the paper. Heat is used to fix the final image on the paper.

Electrostatic Painting

The car panel is given a negative charge and sprayed with positively charged powder paint. The paint spreads out because the positive charges repel each other and are attracted to the negatively charged panel.

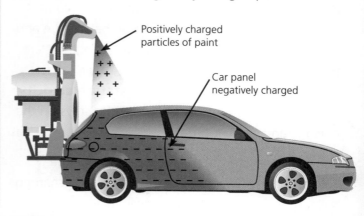

Positively charged particles of paint

Car panel negatively charged

Discharging Unsafe Static

Filling Aircraft Fuel Tanks

During refuelling, the fuel gains electrons from the fuel pipe, making the pipe positively charged and the fuel negatively charged. The resulting voltage between the two can cause a spark (discharge), which could cause a huge explosion. To prevent this, either of the following can be done:
- the fuel tank can be earthed with a copper conductor
- the tanker and the plane can be linked with a copper conductor.

Earthing

Earthing allows a constant safe discharge to occur, to equalise the electron imbalance between the two objects. When earthing occurs, electrons flow from one body to the other to remove the imbalance.

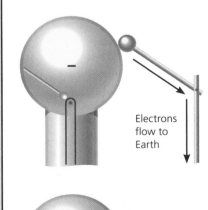

If a conductor touches a negatively charged dome, electrons flow from the dome to Earth, via the conductor, until the dome is completely discharged.

Electrons flow to Earth

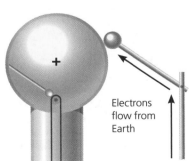

Electrons flow from Earth

If a conductor touches a positively charged dome, electrons flow from Earth to cancel out the positive charge on the dome, until the dome is completely discharged.

Current

Electric current needs a complete circuit to flow. It will then flow continuously until the circuit is broken, e.g. a switch is opened (turned off).

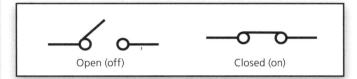

Open (off)   Closed (on)

Current is the **rate of flow of charge**. In a metal, this is a flow of electrons. Electrons have a negative charge. In a complete circuit, they are attracted towards the positive terminal. The flow of electrons is from the negative terminal to the positive terminal (although we draw the current flow in a circuit from the positive terminal to the negative terminal). The greater the flow of electrons (i.e. the more electrons per second), the greater the current.

The total charge that flows in a circuit can be calculated using the following equation:

$$\text{Charge (coulomb, C)} = \text{Current (ampere, A)} \times \text{Time (second, s)}$$

$$\frac{Q}{I \times t}$$

where I is the current and Q is the charge

Example 1

What is the charge that flows in a circuit in a time of 30s when the current is 0.5A?

$$Q = I \times t$$
$$= 0.5 \times 30$$
$$= \textbf{15C}$$

(HT) Example 2

What is the size of the current if 125C of charge flows around a circuit in 25s?

$$I = \frac{Q}{t}$$
$$= \frac{125}{25}$$
$$= \textbf{5A}$$

Cells and Batteries

Cells and **batteries** are sources of **direct current** (d.c.). This means that the current flows in one direction only. In circuit drawings, arrows show direct current flowing from + to –. (However, it is now known that electrons flow from – to +.)

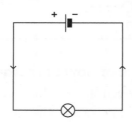

On a cathode ray oscilloscope, d.c. would look like this:

A single dry cell normally gives 1.5 volts. A battery contains two or more single cells (although single cells are commonly referred to as batteries).

The three main types of battery/cell are described in the table below:

Type	Contains...	Used for...
Wet cell rechargeable	lead and acid	cars, industry
Dry cell non-rechargeable	zinc, carbon, manganese or mercury, lithium	torches, clocks, radios, hearing aids, pacemakers
Dry cell rechargeable	nickel, cadmium, lithium	mobile phones, power tools

Non-rechargeable batteries are not beneficial to the environment because:

- the energy needed to make a cell is 50 times greater than the energy it produces
- less than 5% of dry cells are recycled (compared to 90% of wet-cell car batteries)
- the UK produces about 30 000 tonnes of waste dry cells every year (more than 20 cells per household)
- toxic chemicals such as mercury, cadmium and lead can leak into the ground, causing pollution.

Governments are starting to tackle this problem; various schemes for safe disposal (used batteries should not be placed in dustbins) and recycling are being discussed. Rechargeable batteries are one alternative.

P2 Topic 2: Controlling and Using Electric Current

This topic looks at:
- what is meant by potential difference
- how to use an ammeter and voltmeter in a circuit
- how current depends on resistance
- the use of various components
- the heating effect of an electric current

Potential Difference (Voltage)

When current is flowing, energy is transferred from the cell to the circuit components (devices). The electric current will flow through an electrical component if there is a **voltage** (**potential difference**, p.d.) across the ends of the component.

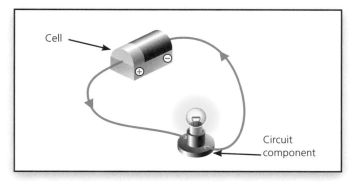

Cell

Circuit component

The atoms of all materials contain electrons but they are normally strongly bound by attraction to the positive nucleus of the atom. In metals (e.g. copper) some of the electrons are less tightly bound (free electrons) and are able to move between the atoms within the metal, making metals good **conductors**.

When a conductor (e.g. a piece of copper wire) is connected to a d.c. supply, the potential difference (voltage) drives the electrons along the conductor. This is an electric current. The greater the potential difference, the greater the electron flow (or 'drift') and the greater the current.

HT The potential difference is the energy (in joules) that is transferred per unit charge (in coulombs) that passes through a source or component.

This means that the volt is a joule per coulomb.

$$\text{Volt} = \frac{\text{Joule}}{\text{Coulomb}}$$

Example

What is the potential difference across a component if 100J of energy is transferred when 25C of charge flows through it?

$$\text{Potential difference} = \frac{100}{25}$$

$$= 4V$$

Circuit Symbols

You should know the following standard symbols:

Cell	
Battery (2 or more cells joined together)	
a.c. supply	
Resistor	
Variable resistor	
Light-dependent resistor (LDR)	
Lamp	
Lamp	
Diode	
Thermistor	
Voltmeter	
Ammeter	

Measuring Current and Potential Difference

Current (the rate of flow of charge) is measured using an **ammeter** in units called **amperes** (**amps, A**). The milliamp (mA) is used for very small currents: 1mA = 0.001A ($\frac{1}{1000}$A). To measure the current through a component, the ammeter must be connected in series.

At any point in a series circuit, the rate of electron flow will be the same, so the current and ammeter readings will be the same.

Potential difference (the measure of electrical pressure) is measured in **volts** (V) using a **voltmeter**. Voltmeters must be connected across a component in parallel.

Current and voltage can be measured at the same time.

In the circuit below the voltage across the lamp is 3.0V and the current flowing through it is 0.1A.

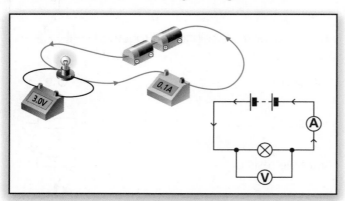

In a circuit the current leaving the battery or cell is the same as the current returning. This is because the electrons that make the current cannot leave the circuit. In the circuit below the current in the main circuit is the sum of the currents in the two branches. Current is conserved at a junction in a circuit.

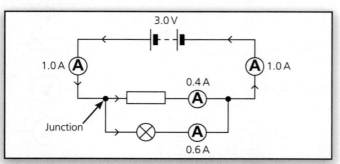

Resistance

Resistance is a measure of how hard it is for a current to flow through a conductor. Resistance is measured in **ohms** (Ω).

Each part of a circuit tries to resist the flow of electrons (current). Even good conductors, such as copper wire, have resistance, but it is so low it can normally be ignored.

Insulators have resistances that are so large that, under normal circumstances, current cannot flow.

As more components are added into a series circuit, the resistance increases.

The greater the resistance, the smaller the current.

Variable Resistors and Fixed Resistors

A **variable resistor** is a component whose resistance can be altered. By altering the resistance, we can change the current that flows through a component, and the potential difference across a component. This enables a range of outputs to be possible, e.g. a brighter or dimmer light.

A **fixed resistor** has only one value of resistance. In the circuit below, adjusting the variable resistor allows a series of values of current and potential difference to be obtained for the fixed resistor. A fixed resistor of about 10Ω is suitable for this circuit.

A graph of current against potential difference across the fixed resistor will show the relationship between them (see graph on page 66).

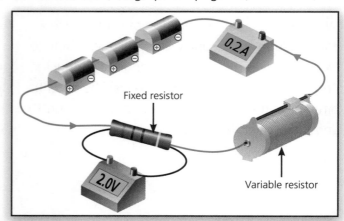

Light-dependent Resistors and Thermistors

Light-dependent resistors and **thermistors** are components whose resistance depends on the surrounding external conditions.

Light-dependent Resistor (LDR)

The resistance of an LDR depends on **light intensity**. Its resistance decreases as light intensity increases.

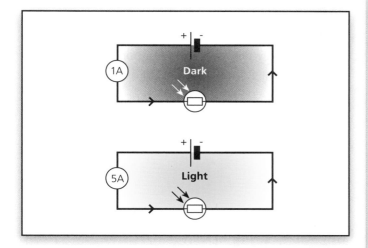

Uses of LDRs: automatic light detectors (e.g. to switch on a light when it gets dark; controlling the exposure time (how long the shutter is open) of a digital camera – in poor light the shutter needs to be open for longer.

Thermistor

For most materials, resistance increases in proportion to an increase in **temperature**. For example, if a light bulb is going to stop working, it normally 'blows' when it is switched on. This is because it is cold so it has a low resistance, which gives a higher current. The high current makes the filament/wire so hot it melts, breaking the circuit.

Thermistors work in the opposite way. Their resistance decreases as the temperature of the thermistor increases.

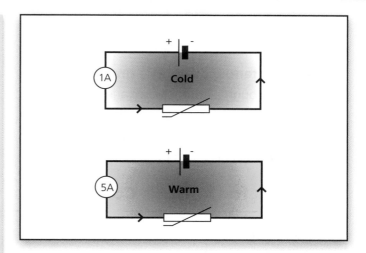

Uses of thermistors: automatic temperature detectors (e.g. frost detectors, fire alarms), measuring engine temperatures of cars (shown on the temperature gauge).

Potential Difference, Current and Resistance

Potential difference, current and resistance are related by the following formula:

| Potential difference (volt, V) | = | Current (ampere, A) | × | Resistance (ohm, Ω) | $\dfrac{V}{I \times R}$ |

where *I* is the current

Example 1

Find the voltage needed across a conductor of resistance 50Ω to cause a current of 2A to pass through it.

$V = I \times R$

$= 2 \times 50$

$= 100V$

HT **Example 2**

A potential difference of 24V placed across a conductor causes a current of 0.2A to flow through the conductor. What is the conductor's resistance?

$R = \dfrac{V}{I}$

$= \dfrac{24}{0.2}$

$= 120Ω$

Current–Potential Difference Graphs

A **current–potential difference graph** shows how the current through a component varies with the voltage across it. If we include a **variable resistor** in a practical circuit, we can get a range of current and voltage readings, which can be used to plot a graph.

If a component such as a resistor or filament lamp is kept at a constant temperature the current is directly proportional to the voltage. The graph of current against voltage will be a straight line passing through the origin. If the component is not kept at a constant temperature, the graph will be curved. This is not the case for a **diode**, as shown in the graph below.

Examples for Various Components

1 Fixed Resistor

If the temperature of the resistor remains constant, equal increases in potential difference across the resistor will produce equal increases in current through the resistor, giving a straight line.

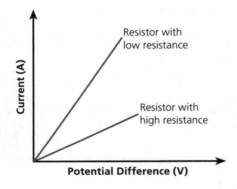

2 Diode

Current only flows in one direction in a diode. A very small current flows until a trigger voltage is reached, after which point current rises rapidly with increase in potential difference (low resistance).

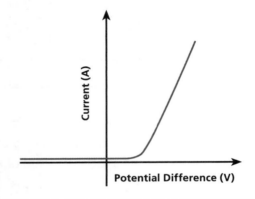

3 Filament Lamp

As the lamp gets hotter, the resistance increases. Look at the dotted lines: equal increases in potential difference give smaller increases in current. (See how the potential difference lines are spaced further apart than the current lines.)

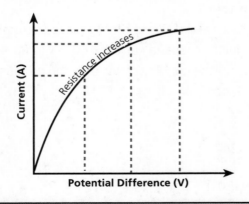

4 Thermistor

As the thermistor gets hotter, the resistance decreases. A small increase in potential difference gives a large increase in current. (See how the current lines are spaced further apart than the potential difference lines.)

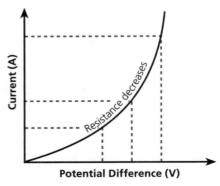

Heating Effect of an Electric Current

When an electric current passes through a resistor, there is an energy transfer and the resistor becomes heated.

> **HT** The moving electrons collide with ions in the lattice of the metal resistor. As a result of these collisions, energy is transferred from electrical to thermal.

This heating effect is used in common electrical appliances such as hairdryers, immersion heaters, kettles and toasters. However, in filament light bulbs, for instance, this heating effect is a distinct disadvantage as a lot of energy is wasted as heat.

Electrical Power

Electrical energy is supplied to an appliance by electric current through a cable. The appliance then transfers the electrical energy into other forms (e.g. light, sound). Some energy will always be 'lost' as heat in the cable.

The **power** of an appliance is determined by the amount of electrical energy transferred in one second. This is measured in watts (W). 1 watt is the rate of transfer of 1 joule of energy per second.

Calculating Power

The power of an appliance is calculated using the formula:

Electrical power (watt, W)	=	Current (ampere, A)	×	Potential difference (volt, V)

$$\frac{P}{I \times V}$$

where I is the current and V is the potential difference

Example

HT A 1.2kW electric fire works best using 5A of current. What should be the voltage of its supply?

(1.2kW = 1200W)

$$V = \frac{P}{I}$$
$$= \frac{1200}{5}$$
$$= \textbf{240 volts}$$

Energy Transfer

The energy transferred to other forms depends on the current, potential difference and the time for which the appliance is switched on.

Energy transferred (joule, J)	=	Current (ampere, A)	×	Potential difference (volt, V)	×	Time (second, s)

$$\frac{E}{I \times V \times t}$$

where I is the current and V is the potential difference

Example

The electric fire in the previous example is switched on for 1 hour.

(a) What electrical energy is transferred? (Time must be in seconds.)

$$E = I \times V \times t$$
$$= 5 \times 240 \times 60 \times 60$$
$$= \textbf{4 320 000J}$$

HT (b) How long (in minutes) would it take to transfer 720 000J?

$$t = \frac{E}{(I \times V)}$$
$$= \frac{720\,000}{(5 \times 240)}$$
$$= \textbf{600s}$$
$$= \textbf{10 minutes}$$

This topic looks at:
- how to interpret graphs
- how to calculate acceleration
- the effect of a resultant force

Speed

One way of describing the movement of an object is by measuring its **speed**, or how fast it is moving.
For example:

- a cyclist travelling at a constant speed of 8 metres per second (8m/s) would travel a distance of 8 metres every second

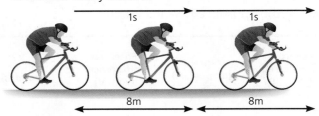

1s   1s

8m   8m

- a car travelling at a constant speed of 60 miles per hour (60mph) would travel a distance of 60 miles every hour.

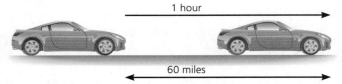

1 hour

60 miles

Speed is measured in **metres per second** (m/s), **kilometres per hour** (km/h) or **miles per hour** (mph).

To calculate speed, use the equation:

$$\text{Speed (m/s)} = \frac{\text{Distance (m)}}{\text{Time (s)}}$$

$$\frac{x}{s \times t}$$

where x is the distance and s is the speed

Example

What is the speed of a car that travels 500m in 25s?

$$s = \frac{x}{t}$$

$$= \frac{500}{25}$$

$$= 20\text{m/s}$$

Distance–Time Graphs

The slope of a **distance–time graph** represents the speed of the object. The steeper the gradient, the greater the speed. The speed can be calculated from the gradient.

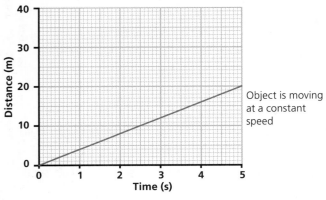

Object is moving at a constant speed

$$\text{Speed} = \frac{20}{5} = 4\text{m/s}$$

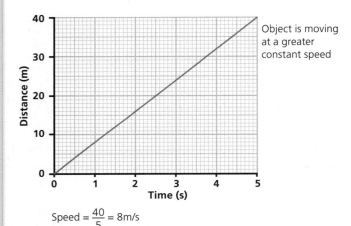

Object is moving at a greater constant speed

$$\text{Speed} = \frac{40}{5} = 8\text{m/s}$$

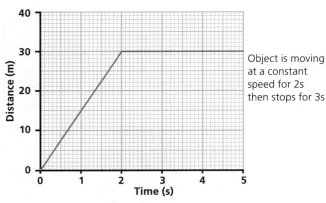

Object is moving at a constant speed for 2s then stops for 3s

$$\text{Speed in first 2s} = \frac{30}{2} = 15\text{m/s}$$

$$\text{Speed in last 3s} = 0\text{m/s}$$

Displacement

Displacement is distance travelled in a stated direction, for example 300m due north. If you walk 2km around a park and end up back where you started, the distance you have travelled is 2km but your displacement is zero. Displacement is a **vector quantity**, because it has both a size and a direction.

Velocity

The **velocity** of a moving object is its speed in a stated direction, for example 40km/h to the east. Like displacement, it is a vector quantity.

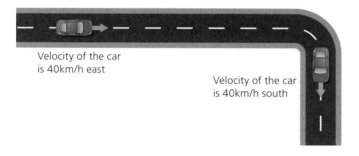

Velocity of the car is 40km/h east

Velocity of the car is 40km/h south

The car in the diagram above may be travelling at a constant speed of 40km/h, but its velocity changes because its direction of movement changes, i.e. from east to south.

The direction of velocity is sometimes indicated by a positive (+) or a negative (−) sign. If one car is travelling at +40mph and another is travelling at −40mph they are simply travelling in opposite directions.

Acceleration

The **acceleration** of an object is the rate at which its velocity changes. In other words, it is a measure of how quickly an object is speeding up or slowing down. This change can be in magnitude (size) and/or direction, so acceleration is a vector quantity.

Acceleration is measured in metres per second, per second or metres per second squared, **m/s²**.

The cyclist in the diagram below increases his velocity by 2m/s every second. So, we can say that the acceleration of the cyclist is 2m/s² (2 metres per second, per second).

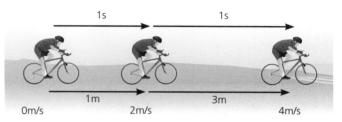

1s   1s

0m/s   1m   2m/s   3m   4m/s

There are two important points to be aware of when measuring acceleration.

1. The cyclist in the diagram is increasing his velocity by the **same amount every second**, however, the **distance travelled each second is increasing**.

2. **Deceleration** is simply a **negative acceleration**. In other words, it describes an object which is slowing down.

If we want to work out the acceleration of any moving object, we need to know two things:

• the change in velocity
• the time taken for the change in velocity.

We can then calculate the acceleration of the object using the following equation:

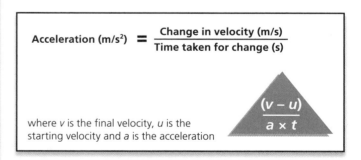

$$\text{Acceleration (m/s}^2) = \frac{\text{Change in velocity (m/s)}}{\text{Time taken for change (s)}}$$

where v is the final velocity, u is the starting velocity and a is the acceleration

$$\frac{(v - u)}{a \times t}$$

Example

A cyclist is travelling at a constant speed of 10m/s. He then accelerates and reaches a velocity of 24m/s after 7s. Calculate his acceleration.

$$\text{Acceleration} = \frac{\text{Change in velocity}}{\text{Time taken}} = \frac{24 - 10}{7}$$

$$= 2\text{m/s}^2$$

Velocity–Time Graphs

The slope of a **velocity–time graph** represents the acceleration of the object: the steeper the gradient, the greater the acceleration. The graphs below show how the acceleration is calculated from a velocity–time graph.

> **HT** You can also calculate the distance travelled from a velocity–time graph. The total distance travelled is given by the area between the line and the axis.

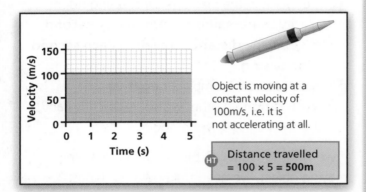

Object is moving at a constant velocity of 100m/s, i.e. it is not accelerating at all.

HT Distance travelled
= 100 × 5 = **500m**

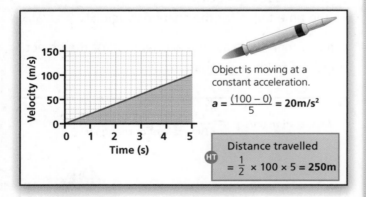

Object is moving at a constant acceleration.

$$a = \frac{(100 - 0)}{5} = 20\text{m/s}^2$$

HT Distance travelled
= $\frac{1}{2}$ × 100 × 5 = **250m**

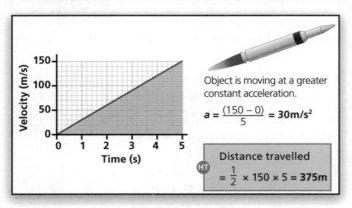

Object is moving at a greater constant acceleration.

$$a = \frac{(150 - 0)}{5} = 30\text{m/s}^2$$

HT Distance travelled
= $\frac{1}{2}$ × 150 × 5 = **375m**

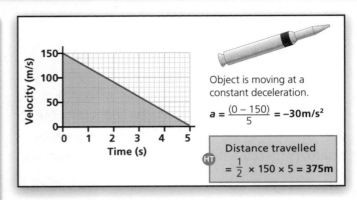

Object is moving at a constant deceleration.

$$a = \frac{(0 - 150)}{5} = -30\text{m/s}^2$$

HT Distance travelled
= $\frac{1}{2}$ × 150 × 5 = **375m**

Forces

Forces are **pushes** or **pulls**, e.g. friction, weight and air resistance. Forces may be different in size and act in different directions. A force can make an object change its speed, its shape, or the direction in which it is moving.

Force is measured in **newtons** (N). Force is a vector quantity, as it has both a size and a direction.

Forces between Two Interacting Objects

When two objects touch, they interact. The interaction involves two forces, acting on the different objects.

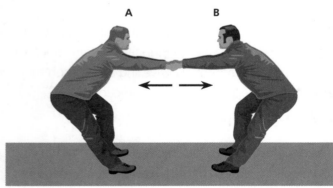

The diagram shows two men pulling against each other. Man A pulls on man B, and man B pulls on man A. Each feels a force from the other; these forces are equal in size and opposite in direction.

In general, when object A exerts a force on object B, this is called an **action** force. Object B will exert a force of equal size and opposite direction on object A, called the **reaction** force. Pairs of action and reaction forces are always forces of the same kind.

Free-Body Force Diagrams

Free-body force diagrams show all the forces acting on an object. Each force is shown by an arrow. The direction of the arrow indicates the direction of the force and the length of the arrow indicates the size of the force. For example:

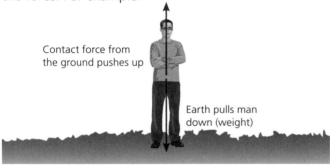

Contact force from the ground pushes up

Earth pulls man down (weight)

This free-body force diagram shows a boat travelling at a constant speed. The forces are all equal so the arrows are all the same length. The forces are balanced, so the boat is in **equilibrium**.

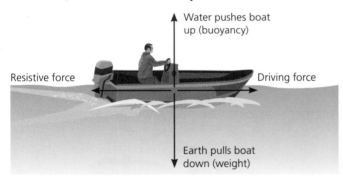

Water pushes boat up (buoyancy)

Resistive force

Driving force

Earth pulls boat down (weight)

How Forces Affect Movement

The movement of an object depends on all the forces acting upon it. The combined effect of these forces is called the **resultant force** and this force affects any subsequent motion of the object.

A moving car has forces acting on it which affect its movement:

Driving force

Direction of movement

Air resistance

Friction

In this diagram, the car exerts a **driving force**. The air resistance and friction are **resistive forces**. The balance of these two types of force dictates the motion of the car.

Look at the diagrams below:

1 Accelerating

When the driving force is greater than the resistive force (i.e. the resultant force is not zero), the car is accelerating. An unbalanced force acts on the car, causing it to speed up, i.e. accelerate.

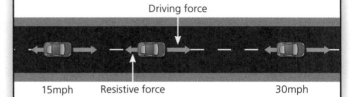

Driving force

15mph   Resistive force   30mph

The driving force is greater than the resistive force.

2 Braking

When the resistive force is greater than the driving force (i.e. the resultant force is not zero), the car is decelerating. An unbalanced force acts on the car, causing it to slow down, i.e. decelerate.

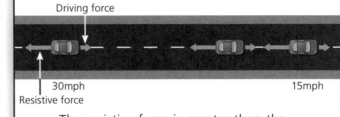

Driving force

30mph   15mph

Resistive force

The resistive force is greater than the driving force.

3 Moving at a Constant Speed

When the driving force is equal to the resistive force (i.e. the resultant force is zero), the car is moving at a constant speed. The forces acting on the car are now balanced.

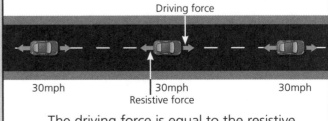

Driving force

30mph   30mph   30mph

Resistive force

The driving force is equal to the resistive force so the acceleration is zero.

Calculating Resultant Force

We can calculate the resultant of several forces by drawing a free-body diagram.

Example

A car has a driving force of 3000N. It is resisted in its movement by air resistance of 150N and friction from the tyres of 850N. Calculate the resultant force for the car.

Draw a free-body diagram.

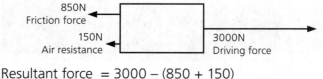

Resultant force = 3000 − (850 + 150)
= **2000N**

Remember that if the resultant force on an object is **zero**, the object will **stay still** or **it will carry on moving at the same velocity**. If the resultant force on an object is **not zero**, it will **accelerate in the direction of the resultant force**.

Force, Mass and Acceleration

If a resultant force acts on an object then the acceleration of the object will depend on:
- the **size** of the resultant force – the bigger the force, the greater the acceleration
- the **mass** of the object – the bigger the mass, the smaller the acceleration. (Mass is the amount of material in an object.)

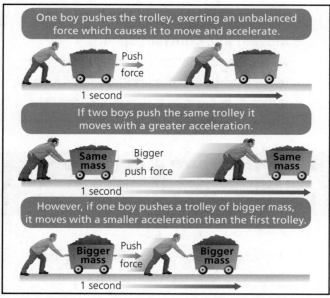

The relationship between force, mass and acceleration is shown in the following formula:

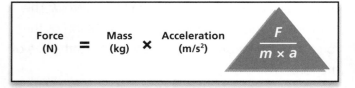

From this, we can define a newton (N) as the force needed to give a mass of one kilogram an acceleration of one metre per second squared ($1m/s^2$).

Example

The trolley below, of mass 400kg, is pushed along the floor with a constant speed, by a man who exerts a push force of 150N.

As the trolley is moving at a constant speed, the forces acting upon it must be balanced. Therefore, the 150N push force must be opposed by 150N of friction.

Another man joins. The trolley now accelerates at $0.5m/s^2$.

As the trolley is now accelerating, the push force must be greater than friction. An unbalanced force now acts.

Calculate the force needed to achieve this acceleration.

Force = Mass × Acceleration
= 400 × 0.5
= **200N**

The total push exerted on the trolley
=   150N   +   200N   = **350N**
   (force equal   (force to provide
   to friction)   acceleration)

Weight and Mass

Weight is a measure of the force exerted on a mass due to the pull of **gravity**. As it is a force, the units are newtons (N).

If you travelled to the Moon, your mass would remain the same as on Earth, but your weight would be less because the **gravitational field strength** of the Moon is much less. The gravitational field strength is measured in newtons per kilogram (N/kg). On Earth it is 10N/kg. (On the Moon it is 1.67N/kg.)

The relationship between weight, mass and gravitational field strength is given by the equation:

$$\text{Weight (N)} = \text{Mass (kg)} \times \text{Gravitational field strength (N/kg)} \qquad \frac{W}{m \times g}$$

Example
Calculate the weight (on Earth) of an object whose mass is 7kg.

$$W = m \times g$$
$$= 7 \times 10$$
$$= 70N$$

Investigating the Relationship between Force, Mass and Acceleration

A dynamics trolley and a runway can be set up to investigate the relationship between force, mass and acceleration. In the investigation we keep the total mass constant, to look at the relationship between force and acceleration.

1 Attach a card with two segments onto a trolley, as shown in the diagram.

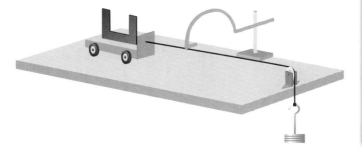

2 Set up a light gate connected to a data logger so the light beam is interrupted by the card. (Input the length of each segment of the card and the distance between them into the datalogger.)

3 Allow the trolley to run down a runway through the light gate and record its acceleration.

4 Adjust the angle of the runway until the acceleration is zero or nearly zero.

5 Pass a length of string over a pulley to a weight hanger, which hangs over the edge of the runway. Attach the other end of the string to the trolley.

6 Tape three 100g masses (3N force) onto the trolley. Record the acceleration, using the weight hanger as a 1N accelerating force. Repeat for forces of 2N, 3N, 4N by transferring the three masses, one at a time, from the trolley to the weight hanger.

7 Plot a graph of acceleration against force.

Terminal Velocity

Falling objects experience two forces:
- the downward force of weight, W (↓), which always stays the same
- the upward force of air resistance, R, or drag (↑).

When a skydiver jumps out of an aeroplane, the speed of his descent can be considered in two separate parts: **before** the parachute opens and **after** the parachute opens (see diagram on page 74).

Terminal Velocity (cont.)

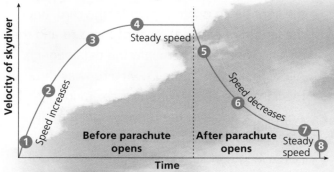

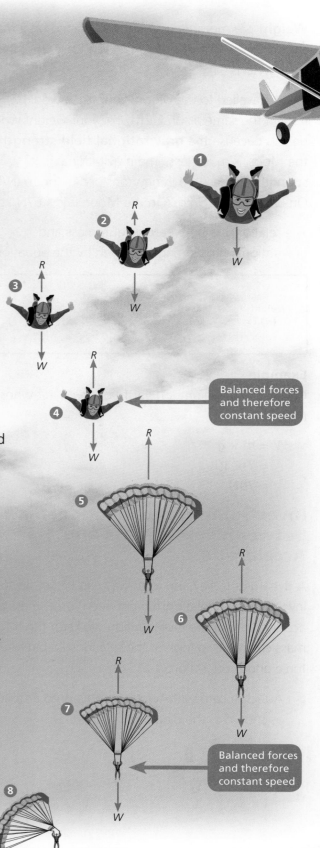

Before the Parachute Opens

When the skydiver jumps, he initially accelerates due to the force of gravity (see **1**). Gravity is a force of attraction that acts between bodies that have mass, e.g. the skydiver and the Earth. The weight (W) of an object is the force exerted on it by gravity. It is measured in newtons (N).

However, as the skydiver falls, he experiences the frictional force of air resistance (R) in the opposite direction. But this is not as great as W so he continues to accelerate (see **2**).

As his speed increases, so does the air resistance acting on him (see **3**), until eventually R is equal to W (see **4**). This means that the resultant force acting on him is now zero and his falling speed becomes constant. This speed is called the **terminal velocity**.

After the Parachute Opens

When the parachute is opened, unbalanced forces act again because the upward force of R is now greatly increased and is bigger than W (see **5**). This causes his speed to decrease and as his speed decreases so does R (see **6**).

Eventually R decreases until it is equal to W (see **7**). The forces acting are once again balanced and for the second time he falls at a steady speed, more slowly than before though, i.e. at a **new terminal velocity**.

He travels at this speed until he lands (see **8**).

Note that these pictures show that there is a sideways force acting on the skydiver. We are only interested in the vertical forces. In the absence of air resistance (i.e. in a vacuum), all falling bodies accelerate at the same rate. If you dropped a feather and a hammer from the same height at the same time on the Moon, both would reach the surface simultaneously.

P2 Topic 4: Momentum, Energy, Work and Power

This topic looks at:
- what is meant by stopping and braking distance
- how momentum relates to safety
- how to calculate power

Stopping Distances

The stopping distance of a vehicle depends on:
- the **thinking distance:** the distance travelled by the vehicle from the point when the driver realises they need to apply the brakes to when they actually apply them
- the **braking distance:** the distance travelled by the vehicle from the point when the driver applies the brakes to when the vehicle actually stops.

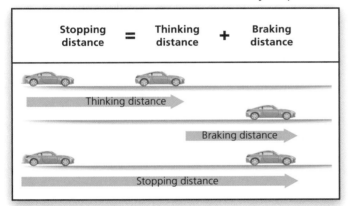

Factors Affecting Stopping Distance

The Speed of the Vehicle

The speed of the vehicle affects both the thinking distance and the braking distance. The chart below shows how the thinking distance and braking distance of a vehicle under normal driving conditions depend on the speed of the vehicle.

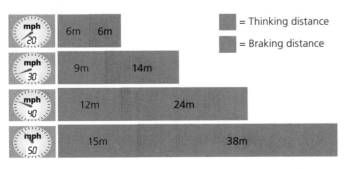

The Mass of the Vehicle

The mass of a vehicle affects the braking distance only. It has no effect on the thinking distance. If the mass of the vehicle is increased, e.g. by passengers or baggage, it has greater kinetic (movement) energy, which increases the braking distance (see page 80).

The Conditions of the Vehicle and the Road

The vehicle may have worn tyres, or the road conditions may be wet, icy or uneven. All these conditions will affect the friction between the tyres and the road and, therefore, the braking distance.

The Driver's Reaction Time

The driver's **reaction time**, i.e. the time taken from the point the driver realises they need to apply the brakes to when they actually apply them, affects the thinking distance only. It has no effect on the braking distance. The following would increase the reaction time of the driver: drinking alcohol; taking drugs; being tired; being distracted by the surroundings.

Investigating Friction

Some simple apparatus can be used to investigate friction between surfaces.

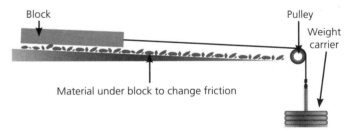

1. Set up a wooden block on a level or slightly sloping surface, as shown.
2. Fix a string to the block. Attach this to a weight carrier hanging vertically over a pulley at the end of the slope (or attach the string to a newton meter).
3. The weight hanger (or the newton meter, pulled parallel to the slope) exerts a force on the block. Record the force needed to keep the block moving steadily. (Remember that weight (N) = mass (kg) × 10 (N/kg).)
4. Repeat the experiment with, for example, water to reduce the friction and sand or sandpaper to increase friction.

Momentum

Momentum is a measure of the state of movement of an object. It is dependent on two things:

- the **mass** of the object (kg)
- the **velocity** of the object (m/s).

Momentum is a vector quantity since velocity is a vector. Therefore, the direction of the momentum is important.

The momentum of an object can be calculated using the following equation:

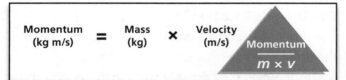

| Momentum (kg m/s) | = | Mass (kg) | × | Velocity (m/s) |

$$\frac{Momentum}{m \times v}$$

Example 1

A railway truck with a mass of 40 tonnes is travelling with a uniform velocity of 15m/s. Calculate the truck's momentum.

Momentum = Mass × Velocity
= (40 × 1000) × 15
= **600 000kg m/s**

> Mass must be in kg: 1 tonne = 1000kg

When two bodies travelling along the same straight path collide, **the total momentum before the collision is always equal to the total momentum after the collision**.

Example 2

Two cars are heading towards each other.

Car A has a mass of 750kg and is travelling at a constant speed of 30m/s due north. Car B has a mass of 1000kg and is travelling at a constant speed of 25m/s due south.

(a) Calculate their total momentum.

Momentum of car A = 750 × 30
= **22 500kg m/s**

Momentum is a vector quantity so one direction has to be called 'positive', say toward the north. The opposite direction is then the 'negative' direction. In this case, car B's momentum is said to be negative.

Momentum of car B = –1000 × 25
= **–25 000kg m/s**
Total momentum = 22 500 + (–25 000)
= **–2500kg m/s**
(towards the south, since the answer is negative).

(b) State their total momentum after they collide.

The total momentum after the collision has to be the same as before the collision. So the answer is **2500kg m/s** towards the south.

When a force acts on a moving object, or a stationary object that is capable of moving, the object will experience a change in momentum.

HT Force and momentum are related by the following equation:

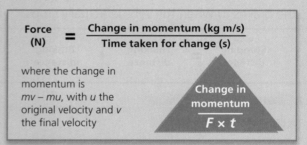

| Force (N) | = | $\dfrac{\text{Change in momentum (kg m/s)}}{\text{Time taken for change (s)}}$ |

where the change in momentum is $mv - mu$, with u the original velocity and v the final velocity

$$\frac{\text{Change in momentum}}{F \times t}$$

Example

A car of mass 1000kg is travelling at 10m/s. 5 seconds later it is travelling at 20m/s.

(a) Calculate the change in momentum.

Start momentum = mu
= 1000 × 10
= 10 000kg m/s
Finish momentum = mv
= 1000 × 20
= 20 000kg m/s
Change in momentum = 20 000 – 10 000
= **10 000kg m/s**

(b) Calculate the force produced by this change in momentum.

$$\text{Force} = \frac{\text{Change in momentum}}{\text{Time taken for change}}$$
$$= \frac{10\,000}{5}$$
$$= \textbf{2000N}$$

Collisions and Safety Technology

In the event of a collision, if the time taken for the body's momentum to reach zero increases, then the forces acting on it can also be reduced. In a car, this is achieved using safety features such as seat belts, air bags and **crumple zones**: instead of coming to an immediate halt, there are a few seconds in which momentum is reduced. This means that the rate at which the momentum changes is reduced. Therefore, the force on the passengers is also reduced, resulting in less serious injuries.

Safety Technology

Cars have lots of safety features to try to minimise injury and reduce the number of deaths.
For example:

- Crumple zones are areas of a vehicle that are designed to deform and crumple in a collision, increasing the time interval for the change in momentum. This means the force exerted on the people inside the car will be reduced, which results in less serious injuries.
- Cushioning during impact (e.g. air bags, soft seats). These reduce the rate at which the momentum changes and so reduce the force exerted. (This is also why delicate articles are wrapped in bubble wrap when they are sent by post.)

- Seat belts lock when the car slows or stops abruptly, but the material of the belt is designed to stretch slightly. This reduces the rate of change of momentum and so reduces the force on the passenger.

Wearing a seat belt whilst travelling in a motor vehicle greatly reduces the chance of death in the event of an accident. In 1992, it became compulsory for all front passengers to wear seat belts, and this led to a massive decline in the number of accident fatalities. The number of fatalities was reduced again following the introduction of compulsory seat belts for all rear passengers in 1994.

Investigating Crumple Zones

One way to investigate crumple zones is to use a dynamics trolley on a sloping surface.

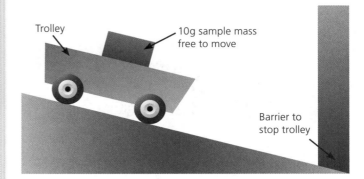

Trolley
10g sample mass free to move
Barrier to stop trolley

1. Place a 10g mass on top of the trolley and allow the trolley to roll down the slope to hit the barrier (e.g. a pile of books) at the end. The 10g mass simulates a person in the car. What happens when the trolley hits the barrier?
2. Now repeat the experiment, using various materials to act as crumple zones; for example, cloth, bubble wrap or polystyrene tied around the front of the trolley. Observe how effective these are at reducing the forces on the passenger. (In this case, the force on the passenger is shown by how far the 10g mass moves when the trolley hits the barrier.)

Work

When a force moves an object, **work** is done on the object, resulting in the **transfer of energy** where:

Work done (J)	**=**	Energy transferred (J)

Work done, force and distance moved are related by the following equation:

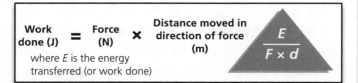

Work done (J)	**=**	Force (N)	**×**	Distance moved in direction of force (m)

where E is the energy transferred (or work done)

$$\frac{E}{F \times d}$$

Example

250N push

A man pushes a car with a steady force of 250N. The car moves a distance of 20m. How much work does the man do?

Work done = Force applied × Distance moved

= 250 × 20

= 5000J (or 5kJ)

So, 5000J of **work has been done** and 5000J of **energy has been transferred**, since work done is equal to energy transferred.

Power

Power is the **rate of doing work** or the **rate of transfer of energy**. The greater the power, the more work is done every second.

Power is measured in **watts (W)** or **joules per second (J/s)**. 1 watt = 1 joule per second.

If two men of the same weight race up the same hill, they do the same amount of work to reach the top.

However, since one man has done the work in a **shorter time**, he has the **greater power**.

Power, work done and time taken are related by the equation:

Power (W)	**=**	$\dfrac{\text{Work done (J)}}{\text{Time taken (s)}}$

$$\frac{E}{P \times t}$$

Example

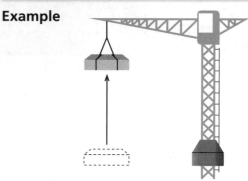

A crane lifts a load of 20 000N through a distance of 10m in 4s. Calculate the output power of the crane.

First, work out how much work the crane does against gravity, then find the power.

Work done = Force applied × Distance moved

= 20 000 × 10

= 200 000J ← The load has now gained this amount of energy

$$\text{Power} = \frac{\text{Work done}}{\text{Time taken}}$$

$$= \frac{200\,000}{4}$$

= 50 000W (or J/s)

(or P = 50kW, since 1kW = 1000W)

Gravitational Potential Energy

An object lifted above the ground gains **potential energy** (PE), often called **gravitational potential energy** (GPE). The additional height gives it the potential to do work when it falls, e.g. a diver on a diving board has gravitational potential energy.

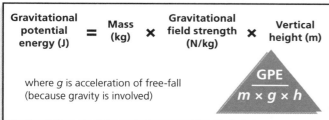

Gravitational potential energy (J)	=	Mass (kg)	×	Gravitational field strength (N/kg)	×	Vertical height (m)

where g is acceleration of free-fall (because gravity is involved)

$$\frac{GPE}{m \times g \times h}$$

Acceleration of free-fall is also referred to as **gravitational field strength** (g), which (we can assume) is a constant and has a value of 10N/kg. This means that every 1kg of matter near the surface of the Earth experiences a downwards force of 10N due to gravity.

Example

A skier of mass 80kg gets on a ski lift, which takes him from a height of 100m to a height of 300m above ground. By how much does his gravitational potential energy increase?

GPE = $m \times g \times h$

   = 80 × 10 × (300 − 100)

   = 80 × 10 × 200

   = 160 000J (or 160kJ, since 1kJ = 1000J)

Kinetic Energy

Kinetic energy is the energy an object has because of its movement. If it is moving, it has kinetic energy, e.g. a moving car or lorry has kinetic energy.

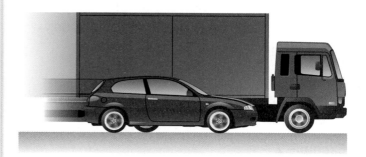

Kinetic energy (J)	=	$\frac{1}{2}$	×	Mass (kg)	×	Velocity² (m/s)²

$$\frac{KE}{\frac{1}{2} \times m \times v^2}$$

Example 1

A car of mass 1000kg is moving at a constant speed of 10m/s. How much kinetic energy does it have?

Kinetic energy = $\frac{1}{2}$ × **Mass** × **Velocity²**

   = $\frac{1}{2}$ × 1000 × $(10)^2$

   = $\frac{1}{2}$ × 1000 × 100

   = 50 000J

Example 2

A lorry of mass 2050kg is moving at a constant speed of 7m/s. How much kinetic energy does it have?

Kinetic energy = $\frac{1}{2}$ × **Mass** × **Velocity²**

   = $\frac{1}{2}$ × 2050 × $(7)^2$

   = $\frac{1}{2}$ × 2050 × 49

   = 50 225J

Conservation of Energy

There are many other forms of energy: heat energy, chemical energy, nuclear energy, wave energy, sound energy, etc.

The principle of the **conservation of energy** states that energy cannot be created or destroyed, only transferred from one form into another.

Example 1
When a diver jumps off a diving board, gravitational potential energy transfers into kinetic energy.

Example 2
In a hydro-electric generating plant, gravitational potential energy transfers into kinetic energy, then into electrical energy.

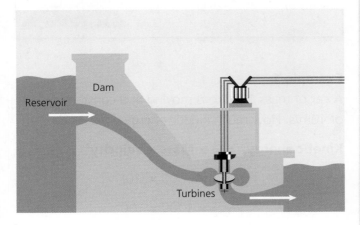

Example 3
Light energy from the Sun transfers to electrical energy in a solar panel.

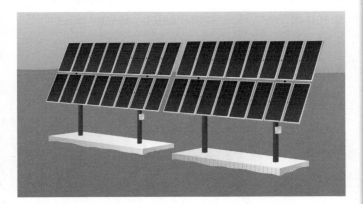

Example 4
In a light bulb, electrical energy transfers into heat energy and light energy.

Braking Distance and Velocity

When a vehicle is brought to a stop, work has to be done by the brakes. The kinetic energy that the vehicle has must be reduced to zero.

The work done by the brakes must equal the initial kinetic energy (which is transferred into heat energy in the brakes).

Work done = Kinetic energy

Since kinetic energy = $\frac{1}{2}$ × mass × velocity^2, this means that the braking distance of the vehicle depends on the square of its initial velocity.

Example
A car of mass 1000kg is travelling at 20m/s. The car brakes and is brought to a stop in a distance of 40m.

What force did the brakes apply?

Work done by the brakes = Kinetic energy lost

$$F \times d = \tfrac{1}{2} \times \text{mass} \times \text{velocity}^2$$

$$F = \frac{\tfrac{1}{2} \times \text{mass} \times \text{velocity}^2}{d}$$

$$F = \frac{\tfrac{1}{2} \times 1000 \times 20^2}{40}$$

$$= \frac{\tfrac{1}{2} \times 1000 \times 400}{40}$$

$$= \textbf{5000N}$$

Nuclear Fission and Nuclear Fusion P2

P2 Topic 5: Nuclear Fission and Nuclear Fusion

This topic looks at:
- what radioactive isotopes are
- how nuclear reactions can be controlled
- what conditions are needed for fusion to occur

Isotopes

The **mass number (or nucleon number)** of an element is the total number of protons and neutrons in the nucleus of an atom.

The **atomic number (or proton number)** of an element is the number of protons in the nucleus of an atom.

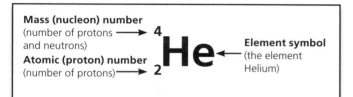

All atoms of a particular element have the same number of protons. The number of protons defines the element. However, some atoms of the same element can have different numbers of neutrons – these are called **isotopes**. Oxygen has three isotopes: oxygen-16 (^{16}O), oxygen-17 (^{17}O) and oxygen-18 (^{18}O):

$$^{16}_{8}O \quad ^{17}_{8}O \quad ^{18}_{8}O$$

8 neutrons   9 neutrons   10 neutrons

Although the atomic (proton) number is the same in all isotopes of an element, the mass (nucleon) number will vary. The difference between the mass number and the atomic number tells us how many neutrons there are in each isotope of the element.

Radiation

Some substances contain isotopes with **unstable nuclei**. An atom is unstable when its nucleus contains too many or too few neutrons.

Unstable nuclei split up or disintegrate, emitting **radiation**. The atoms of such isotopes disintegrate randomly and are said to be **radioactive**.

There are three main types of radioactive radiation:
- **Alpha** (α) – an alpha particle is a helium nucleus (a particle made up of two protons and two neutrons).
- **Beta** (β) – a beta particle is a high-energy electron.
- **Gamma** (ϒ) – a gamma ray is high-frequency electromagnetic radiation.

A radioactive isotope will emit one or more of the three types of radiation from its nucleus.

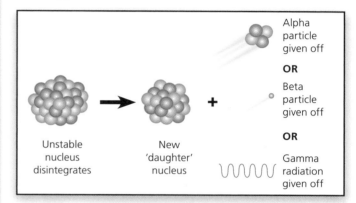

Radiation and Ionisation

A radioactive substance is capable of emitting one of the three types of radiation: **alpha particles, beta particles** or **gamma rays**. When this radiation collides with neutral atoms or molecules in a substance, the atoms or molecules may become charged due to electrons being 'knocked out' of their structure during the collision. This alters their structure, leaving them as **ions** (atoms with an electrical charge) or **charged particles**. Atoms can also become (negatively) charged by gaining electrons.

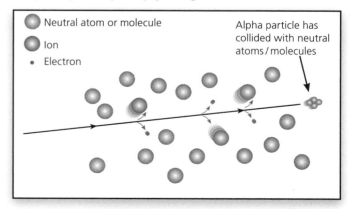

Radiation and Ionisation (cont.)

Alpha particles, beta particles and gamma rays are therefore known as **ionising radiations** (they are randomly emitted from the unstable nuclei of radioactive isotopes). The relative ionising power of each type of radiation is different, as is its power to penetrate different materials, and its range in air.

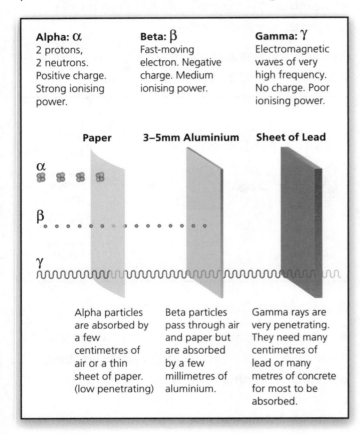

Alpha: α
2 protons, 2 neutrons. Positive charge. Strong ionising power.

Beta: β
Fast-moving electron. Negative charge. Medium ionising power.

Gamma: γ
Electromagnetic waves of very high frequency. No charge. Poor ionising power.

Paper — **3–5mm Aluminium** — **Sheet of Lead**

Alpha particles are absorbed by a few centimetres of air or a thin sheet of paper. (low penetrating)

Beta particles pass through air and paper but are absorbed by a few millimetres of aluminium.

Gamma rays are very penetrating. They need many centimetres of lead or many metres of concrete for most to be absorbed.

Energy Trapped Inside the Atom

Large, **heavy** atoms, such as atoms of uranium, can become more stable (this is known as **radioactive decay**) by losing an alpha or beta particle, a process which occurs naturally. Stability can be gained more quickly by bombarding the nucleus of the atom of uranium with neutrons in a process called **nuclear fission**. The tiny amount of mass lost in the fission process is translated into an enormous amount of energy.

Nuclear Fission

Nuclear fission is the process of **splitting atomic nuclei**. It is used in nuclear reactors to produce energy to make electricity. The two substances commonly used are uranium-235 (U-235) and plutonium-239 (Pu-239). Unlike radioactive decay, which is a random process, nuclear fission is caused by the bombardment of the nucleus of the atom with a **source of neutrons**.

The products of the collision are two smaller (**daughter**) nuclei and two or three other neutrons, along with the release of an enormous amount of energy. If 235g of U-235 were fissioned, the energy produced would be the same as burning 800 000kg of coal!

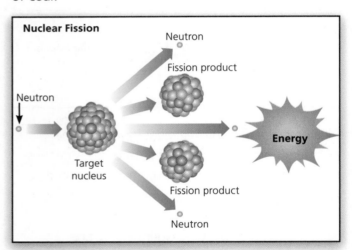

Nuclear Fission

Neutron

Fission product

Neutron

Energy

Target nucleus

Fission product

Neutron

The products of nuclear fission are radioactive. They remain radioactive for a long time, which means they must be stored or disposed of very carefully.

Chain Reactions

Suppose a neutron colliding with a U-235 nucleus produces two further neutrons. These neutrons can go on to interact with further U-235 nuclei, producing four neutrons, then eight, then 16, then 32 and so on.

Each fission reaction produces an enormous amount of energy in a process called a **chain reaction**.

The diagram below shows the chain reaction for U-235 when two neutrons are produced in each fission.

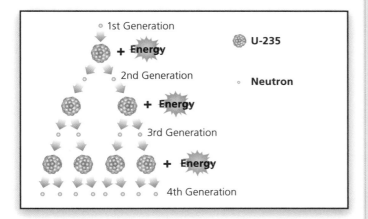

Atomic Bombs and Nuclear Reactors

Manipulating the chain reaction allows it to be used in two different ways:

1 Uncontrolled Chain Reaction
- Neutrons bombard pure uranium nuclei.
- An enormous amount of energy is released.
- An enormous amount of radiation is released.

This forms an **atomic bomb**.

2 Controlled Chain Reaction
- Neutrons bombard a mixture of U-235 and U-238 nuclei.
- The heat produced is used to make steam to generate electricity.

This forms a **nuclear reactor**.

Nuclear Reactors

The diagram below shows a **pressurised water reactor** (**PWR**). The reactor is inside a steel pressure vessel and is surrounded by thick concrete to absorb radiation. Heat (thermal energy) from the PWR is carried away by water that is boiled to produce steam. The steam drives the turbines that generate electricity (electrical energy). The steam cools to produce water, which is then returned to the reactor to be re-heated.

The reactor cannot explode like an atomic bomb because the U-235 nuclei are too far apart for an uncontrolled chain reaction to occur.

The chain reaction is basically controlled in two different ways:

Control rods are used to absorb some of the neutrons that are produced in the fission process. This means there are fewer neutrons to cause further fission. The rods can be raised or lowered into the reactor core. Raising the rods will increase the power of the reactor, while lowering them will reduce it.

A **moderator**, which is often water, slows down the fast neutrons. Slower neutrons are more likely to cause fission so the use of a moderator increases the power output of the reactor.

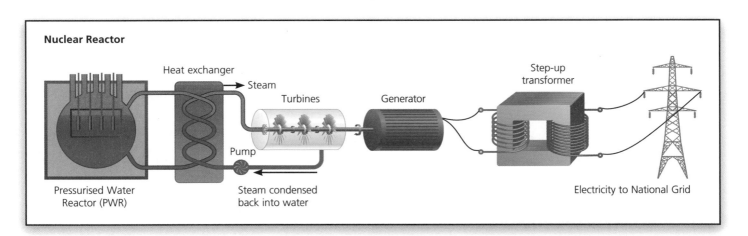

Nuclear Fusion

Nuclear fusion involves the joining together of two or more light atomic nuclei to form a larger atomic nucleus. It takes a huge amount of heat and energy to force the nuclei to fuse. This means that fusion is not a practical way to generate power. However, for each kilogram of fuel, the energy produced by fusion is significantly greater than that produced by fission. If we could somehow harness the energy from fusion, we would have unlimited amounts of energy and our energy problems would be solved.

The energy produced by the Sun, and similar stars, comes from the fusion of two 'heavy' isotopes of hydrogen called **deuterium** and **tritium**.

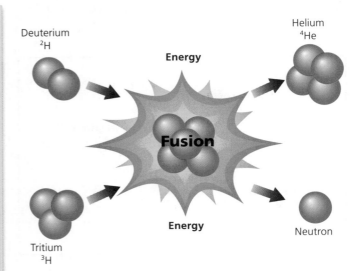

Remember that fission is the splitting of heavy nuclei. Fusion is the joining of light nuclei together.

HT Conditions for Nuclear Fusion

Atomic nuclei repel each other because protons have positive charge. For fusion to take place, the nuclei have to be close together. At extremely high temperatures, nuclei move very fast. If they are moving fast enough, when they collide they will have sufficient energy to overcome the electrostatic repulsion and get close enough to fuse together. At high pressures, there are a lot of nuclei within a small volume to make sure that collisions can happen. These conditions are found in the Sun.

The practical problems involved in producing energy from fusion to make a practical and cost-effective form of power are:

1 **Temperature**
The fuel needs to be heated to 100 million degrees Celsius. This is about six times hotter than the interior of our Sun!

2 **Pressure**
Extremely high pressures are needed to force the nuclei into a very small space.

3 **Confinement**
At such extreme temperatures and pressures, no ordinary vessel can be used to contain (or confine) the fuel. One solution is to use large magnetic and electric fields instead.

Cold Fusion

In 1989, it was reported that an electrolysis experiment carried out at the University of Utah in the USA had produced more heat than would be expected. In fact, the researchers maintained that the amount of heat could only be explained as the result of a nuclear process. Additionally, some by-products of nuclear fusion, such as neutrons, were claimed to have been detected.

As this experiment was conducted at room temperatures, it was called 'cold fusion'.

This caused an incredible amount of excitement at the time. However, despite many hundreds of scientists around the world repeating the original experiment, the results have not been reproduced.

Scientific theories such as cold fusion are not accepted until they have been proven by many scientists who make up the world scientific community.

P2 Topic 6: Advantages and Disadvantages of Using Radioactive Materials

This topic looks at:

- where radioactivity comes from
- how radioactivity decays
- how radiation affects living organisms
- the advantages and disadvantages of using nuclear power

Background Radiation

Background radiation is radiation that occurs all around us. It only provides a very small dose so there is little danger to our health. The pie chart below shows the sources of background radiation.

Key:

Radon gas (50%)
A colourless, odourless gas produced during the radioactive decay of uranium, which is found naturally in granite rock. Released at the surface of the ground, it poses a threat if it builds up in a home, e.g. it can result in lung cancer. The amount of radon varies. Areas with higher concentrations tend to be built on granite, e.g. Devon, Cornwall and Edinburgh.

Medical (12%)
Mainly X-rays.

Nuclear industry (less than 1%)

Cosmic rays (10%)
From outer space and the Sun.

From food (12%)

Gamma (γ) rays (15%)
From rock, soil and building products.

13% of radiation is from manufactured sources

87% of radiation is from natural sources

Radioactive Decay and Half-life

The **activity** of a radioactive isotope is the average number of disintegrations that occur every second. It is measured in **becquerels** and decreases over a period of time.

In a certain time interval, the same fraction of nuclei will **decay** (change to other isotopes or elements). This fraction stays constant.

The **half-life** of a radioactive isotope is a measurement of the rate of radioactive decay, i.e. the time it takes for half the undecayed nuclei to decay.

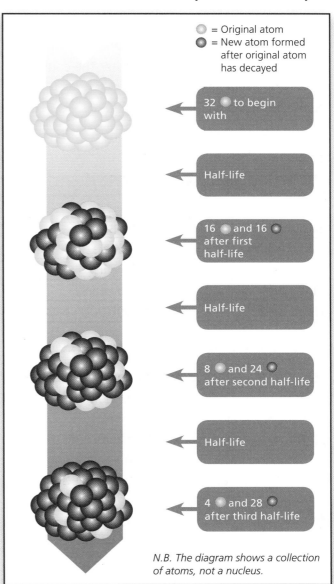

○ = Original atom
◉ = New atom formed after original atom has decayed

32 ○ to begin with

Half-life

16 ○ and 16 ◉ after first half-life

Half-life

8 ○ and 24 ◉ after second half-life

Half-life

4 ○ and 28 ◉ after third half-life

N.B. The diagram shows a collection of atoms, not a nucleus.

If a radioactive isotope has a very long half-life, then it remains active for a very long time.

Finding Half-life from a Graph

The graph below shows the **count rate** against time for the radioactive material iodine-128 (I-128). The count rate is the average number of radioactive emissions.

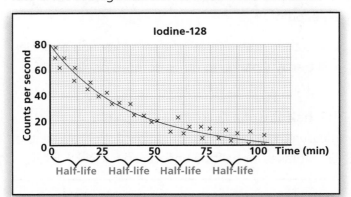

As time goes on, there are fewer and fewer unstable atoms left to decay. After 25 minutes the count rate has fallen to half its original value. Therefore, iodine-128 has a half-life of 25 minutes.

The table below shows the half-lives of some other radioactive elements.

Material	Half-life
Radon-222	4 days
Strontium-90	28 years
Radium-226	1600 years
Carbon-14	5730 years
Plutonium-239	24 400 years
Uranium-235	700 000 000 years

Simulating Radioactive Decay

Obtain as many dice as possible for this experiment. The more dice you use, the closer the simulation to radioactive decay.

1. Throw the dice on to a surface and count the number of dice with, say, the number 1 uppermost.
2. Record the number of dice showing 1 and then remove all of those dice.
3. Repeat the process again (about four times) with the remaining dice.
4. Plot a graph of the number of dice left (on the vertical axis) against the number of throws.
5. Draw a smooth best-fit curve.
6. Find the 'half-life' as above.

Using Half-life

Knowledge about the half-lives of radioactive elements can be used to date certain materials by measuring the amount of radiation they emit.

Materials that can be dated include:
- very old samples of wood
- remains of prehistoric bones
- certain types of rock.

This is because certain materials contain radioactive isotopes which decay to produce **stable isotopes**. If we know the **proportion** of each of these isotopes and the half-life of the radioactive isotope, then it is possible to date the material.

For example:
- Igneous rocks may contain uranium isotopes, which decay via a series of relatively short-lived isotopes to produce stable isotopes of lead. This takes a long time because uranium has a very long half-life.
- Wood and bones contain the carbon-14 (C-14) isotope, which decays when the organism dies.

Example

A very small sample of dead wood has an activity of 1000 becquerels. The same mass of 'live' wood has an activity of 4000 becquerels. If the half-life of carbon-14 is 5730 years, calculate the age of the wood.

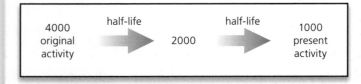

The activity of the dead wood is $\frac{1}{4}$ of that of the live wood. The carbon-14 in the dead wood has therefore been decaying for two half-lives ($\frac{1}{4} = \frac{1}{2} \times \frac{1}{2}$).

So, the age of the wood is two half-lives

$$= 2 \times 5730$$

$$= \textbf{11 460 years}$$

Effect of Ionising Radiation on Living Organisms

Ionising radiation can damage cells and tissues, causing cancer, including leukaemia (cancer of the blood), or **mutations** (changes) in the cells, and can result in the birth of deformed babies in future generations. This is why precautions must always be taken when dealing with any type of radiation.

With all types of radiation, the greater the dose received, the greater the risk of damage. However, the damaging effect depends on whether the radiation source is outside or inside the body.

If the source is outside the body:
- alpha (α) radiation is stopped by the skin and cannot penetrate into the body
- beta (β) and gamma (γ) radiation and X-rays can penetrate into the body to reach the cells of organs, where they are absorbed.

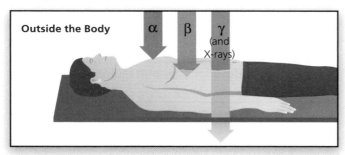

If the source is inside the body:
- alpha (α) radiation causes most damage as it is entirely absorbed by cells, causing the most ionisation
- beta (β) and gamma (γ) radiation and X-rays cause less damage as they are less likely to be absorbed by cells.

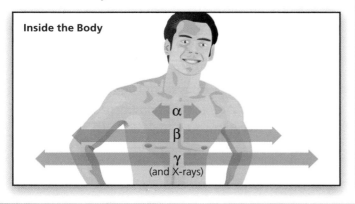

Precautions

People working with ionising radiation (for example, in the nuclear industry and radiographers in hospitals), may need to wear protective clothing. The amount of exposure to radiation is monitored on a daily basis. Some highly radioactive materials may be handled remotely. For hospital patients undergoing treatment, the amount of exposure is limited as much as possible. Treatment plans include the type of radiation used, its half-life and how long the procedure takes.

Uses of Radiation

Ionising radiation can be used beneficially, for example, to treat **tumours** and cancers. This is done by one of the following methods:
- implanting a radioactive material in the area to be treated
- dosing the patient with a radioactive isotope
- exposing the patient to precisely focused beams of radiation from a machine such as an X-ray machine.

Radiotherapy slows down the spread of cancerous cells so it is used to treat cancer.

Gamma Rays and X-rays

Gamma rays and X-rays are forms of electromagnetic radiation. Gamma rays are emitted by highly excited atomic nuclei. X-rays can be produced by means of a medical X-ray tube and are emitted when fast-moving electrons hit a metal target. Low-energy gamma rays and X-rays can pass through flesh but not bone, which is why bones show up on an X-ray photograph. Gamma rays and X-rays have weak ionising power but both can damage living cells.

Sterilisation of Medical Instruments

Gamma rays can be used to sterilise medical instruments because germs and bacteria are destroyed by them. An advantage of this method is that no heat is required, therefore damage to the instruments is minimised.

Preserving Food

Subjecting food to low doses of radiation kills microorganisms within the food and prolongs its shelf life.

Uses of Radiation (cont.)

Controlling the Thickness of Sheet Materials

When radiation passes through a material, some of it is absorbed. The greater the thickness of the material, the greater the absorption of radiation. This can be used to control the thickness of different manufactured materials, e.g. paper production at a paper mill. If the paper is too thick, then less radiation passes through to the detector and a signal is sent to the rollers, which move closer together.

A beta emitter is used since the paper would absorb all alpha particles and would have no effect at all on gamma rays, regardless of its thickness.

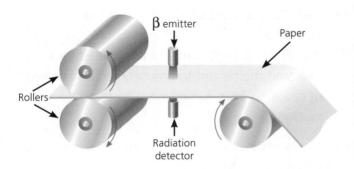

Smoke Detectors

Most smoke alarms contain americium-241, which is an alpha emitter. Emitted alpha particles cause ionisation of the air particles and the ions formed are attracted to the oppositely charged electrodes. This results in a current flowing through the circuit.

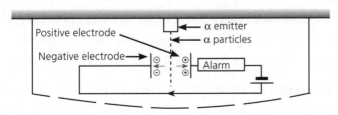

When smoke enters the space between the two electrodes, less ionisation takes place as the alpha particles are absorbed by the smoke particles. A smaller current than normal flows, causing the alarm to sound.

Using Radioactivity: Changing Ideas

1896	Henri Becquerel discovers mysterious rays – radioactivity from uranium.
1901	First therapeutic use of radium.
1908	Radioluminescent paint is invented. This radium-based paint is used, for example, in watches and aircraft instruments. Geiger counter for detecting radioactivity invented.
1920s	Many physicians and corporations begin marketing radioactive substances such as patent medicine and radium-containing waters to be drunk as a tonic.
1927	Herman Muller publishes research to show genetic effects of radioactivity.
1930s	A number of injuries and deaths lead to removal of radium-containing 'medicine' and treatments from the market. The harmful effects of radioluminescent paint become increasingly clear. A notorious case involved a group of women (the 'radium girls') who painted watch-faces and later suffered radiation poisoning after they habitually licked their paintbrushes.
1942	Film badges for checking radioactivity exposure invented.
1945	World's first atomic bomb is exploded.
1949	Radiocarbon dating is developed.
1956	First power station to produce commercial quantities of electricity opened at Calder Hall, UK.
1957	Nuclear bomb fall-out declared harmful to humans.
1963	100 countries sign treaty to ban testing of nuclear weapons in upper atmosphere.
1974	Nuclear reactor at Three Mile Island in the USA melts down, releasing radioactivity into the environment.
1986	Irradiated food available for the first time. At Chernobyl Nuclear Power Plant in the Ukraine, a series of explosions sends large amounts of radioactivity into the atmosphere. Many people in surrounding areas are affected.
1990s	Radiotherapy regularly used in cancer treatment instead of surgery.

Nuclear Power

The use of **nuclear power** has advantages and disadvantages, and the setting up of a nuclear power station in any part of the UK will have a huge environmental and social impact.

Advantages of a Nuclear Power Station

- No greenhouse gas emissions (e.g. carbon dioxide).
- No air pollutants such as carbon monoxide, sulfur dioxide, etc.
- Quantity of waste is small.
- Low fuel costs.
- Local economy could benefit from the many jobs created.

Disadvantages of a Nuclear Power Station

- Risk of a major accident, e.g. Three Mile Island, Chernobyl.
- Nuclear waste is dangerous and long-lived leading to transport and storage problems.
- High construction and maintenance costs.
- Security concerns.
- Large-scale designs – large areas of land used.
- A power station spoils the look of the countryside.
- Wildlife habitats would be destroyed.
- An increase in traffic means an increase in noise and air pollution.

Nuclear Waste

Currently there are a number of possible ways to deal with nuclear waste, depending on its type.

High-level waste – about 1% of the total waste is from spent fuel rods. When they are removed from the core of the reactor, they are highly radioactive and are placed in a pool filled with water. The water cools the rods. The spent fuel rods are placed much further apart than in the reactor, to minimise the chance of fission occurring.

Some ideas for the longer term disposal of spent fuel rods are to bury them under the sea floor, store them underground, or even blast them into space. The most likely possibility is to bury them about a mile underground in special, tightly sealed casks.

Medium-level waste – which accounts for nearly 20% of the total, comes from things such as cladding around the fuel rods and radioactive sludge. This can be contained in stainless steel drums and stored in monitored areas above ground.

Low-level waste – about 80% of all the waste is from items that are only slightly radioactive, such as protective clothing and laboratory equipment. This can be compacted and placed in containers and then stored above ground in special areas.

Questions labelled with an asterisk (*) are ones where the quality of your written communication will be assessed – you should take particular care with your spelling, punctuation and grammar, as well as the clarity of expression, on these questions.

1 Two charged materials are brought near each other. They repel. This means that:

A ☐ they hate each other

B ☐ they have opposite charges

C ☐ one must have a negative charge

D ☐ they have the same type of charge **(1)**

2 Give an example of one occurrence of static electricity. **(1)**

3 What is meant by 'earthing' when referring to static electricity? **(1)**

4 How do you measure potential difference? **(2)**

5 How is a thermistor different from a fixed resistor? **(3)**

6 What p.d. is needed across a resistance of 10Ω to cause a current of 1.5A to flow? **(1)**

7 A car is moving at a constant speed of 20m/s. It then accelerates to a steady speed of 28m/s in a time of 4s. Calculate its acceleration. **(2)**

8 The mass of the car in question 7 is 850kg.

(a) Calculate the resultant force the car's engine provides. **(1)**

(b) The driving force of the engine is 2500N. What is the size of the resistive forces? **(2)**

9 A parachutist jumps from an aeroplane. After a while, she moves at terminal velocity. What does this mean? **(2)**

10 **(a)** The stopping distance is the sum of two distances. What are they called? **(1)**

(b) Name two factors that affect the stopping distance. **(2)**

11 A camper van with mass of 1200kg is travelling along a road at a constant speed of 20m/s.

(a) Calculate its momentum. **(1)**

The camper van collides with a small car travelling in the same direction. Before the two vehicles collide, the momentum of the small car is 12 000kg m/s.

(b) What is the total momentum of the two vehicles before the collision? **(1)**

(c) What is their total momentum after they collide? **(1)**

12 How do crumple zones in the structure of a car help to reduce injuries to passengers? **(3)**

13 An isotope of oxygen has a mass number 17 and an atomic number 8.

   (a) What is the meaning of 'isotope'? **(2)**

   (b) How many electrons does this atom have? **(1)**

   (c) How many neutrons does this atom have? **(1)**

14 Alpha, beta and gamma are three types of nuclear radiation. Which one:

   (a) has the least ionising power? **(1)**

   (b) is stopped by a thin sheet of paper? **(1)**

   (c) has a positive electrical charge? **(1)**

15 **(a)** What is meant by 'background radiation'? **(1)**

   (b) Give one example of a source of background radiation. **(1)**

16 The half-life of a source is 3.5 hours. If the measured count rate at 9am is 1500Bq, at what time will its count rate be 375Bq? **(3)**

17 *It is proposed to build a nuclear power station. It will be built beside the sea not far from a small town. Discuss the arguments for and against. **(6)**

HT

18 Why can refuelling of an aircraft be dangerous? How can the danger be prevented? **(4)**

19 In terms of resistance, explain the difference in the characteristic curve of a filament bulb compared to that for a diode. **(4)**

20 **(a)** Define 'potential difference' in terms of energy. **(2)**

   (b) Hence show that the volt is a joule per coulomb. **(2)**

21 *When an electric current passes through a wire, the wire heats up. Explain why this happens. **(6)**

22 What happens to the forces acting on a skydiver after she opens her parachute? **(3)**

23 A ball of mass 120g is thrown at a wall. The ball hits the wall at a speed of 4m/s. It rebounds straight back at a speed of 3m/s. Calculate:

   (a) the change in momentum **(3)**

   (b) the force that the wall exerts on the ball if it is in contact with the wall for 0.2s. **(2)**

24 A car of mass 1200kg is stopped in a distance of 50m by applying a braking force of 2000N. What is the car's initial velocity? **(4)**

25 *Explain why high temperatures are needed for nuclear fusion to occur. **(6)**

26 The damaging effect of radiation does not depend on whether the source is inside or outside the body. Is this true? Discuss this statement. **(5)**

Answers

Model answers have been provided for the quality of written communication questions that are marked with an asterisk (*). The model answers would score the full 6 marks available. If you have made most of the points given in the model answer and communicated your ideas clearly, in a logical sequence with few errors in spelling, punctuation and grammar, you would get 6 marks. You will lose marks if some of the points are missing, if the answer lacks clarity and if there are serious errors in spelling, punctuation and grammar.

Unit B2

1. (a) **1 mark for component, 1 mark for function, e.g.** Cellulose cell walls for support; Vacuoles to store cell sap; Chloroplasts, which contain chlorophyll, for photosynthesis
   (b) (i) Respiration
       (ii) **Any particularly active cell, e.g.** Sperm cell; Muscle cell

2. Double stranded **(1 mark)**; Coiled into a double helix **(1 mark)**; Has four bases: A, T, C and G **(1 mark)**

3. Removal of a gene from one organism and insertion into another

4. Scientists found a naturally occurring plant resistant to the herbicide **(1 mark)**; and identified the gene responsible for the resistance **(1 mark)**; Vector used to transfer the gene to the embryo crop plant's DNA **(1 mark)**; Crops allowed to grow and are now resistant **(1 mark)**

5. (a) C
   (b) Fear of cloning the 'perfect' race; Possibility of abnormalities occurring in clones; Clones do not have 'parents'
   *(c) Mitosis occurs in most parts of the body. It produces two identical cells. They are diploid (have two sets of chromosomes). Meiosis occurs only in the ovaries and testes. It produces four non-identical cells. They are haploid (have one set of chromosomes).

6. (a) To replace damaged cells and tissues; To treat some diseases
   (b) Some people think that an embryo is an individual life

7. (a) Amino acids
   (b) DNA
   (c) **Any two from:** Enzymes; Hormones; Skin; Hair; Growth; Repair

8. (a) Enzyme is the lock and substrate is the key **(1 mark)**; Substrate fits into the enzyme (like a key in a lock) **(1 mark)**; Enzyme is specific for the substrate (like a lock and key) **(1 mark)**
   (b) High temperatures; Extreme pH
   (c) Substrate no longer fits into the enzyme **(1 mark)**; Key no longer fits into the lock **(1 mark)**

9. (a) Glucose + Oxygen → Carbon dioxide + Water (with Energy released) **(1 mark for reactants, 1 mark for products)**
   (b) The movement of a substance from an area of higher to one of lower concentration down a concentration gradient
   (c) Glucose → Lactic acid (with Energy released) **(1 mark for reactant, 1 mark for product)**
   (d) To repay the 'oxygen debt' to cells

10. (a) **Any suitable answer (1 mark for each characteristic, 1 mark for the reason), e.g.** Lots of internal air spaces to create large surface area
    (b) Carbon dioxide + Water → Glucose + Oxygen **(1 mark for reactants, 1 mark for products)**
    (c) Diffusion of water from an area of higher concentration of water to an area of lower concentration of water across a partially permeable membrane

11. Water enters plants into their roots by osmosis **(1 mark)**; Transported to the leaves in xylem vessels **(1 mark)**; Transport is called transpiration **(1 mark)**; It is driven by evaporation of water vapour though stomata in the leaves **(1 mark)**

12. **(a)** A

(b) A measure of the variety of different types of organism in a habitat or ecosystem

(c) Quadrats placed on the ground to count the number, type or percentage cover of organisms inside them **(1 mark)**; Placement is random or systematic (along a transect) **(1 mark)**; Use many locations to give reliable picture of the habitat **(1 mark)**

13. **(a)** Red blood cells; Platelets; Plasma

(b) Phagocytes; Lymphocyte

14. Tissues: Groups of specialised cells of the same type that complete the same function **(1 mark)**; Organs: Groups of tissues that are joined together to complete a specific function **(1 mark)**; Systems: Groups of organs that work together to complete a specific function **(1 mark)**

15. **(a)** Blood makes two 'loops' as it travels around the body (from heart to lungs to heart to body and back to heart)

*(b) Blood leaves the left ventricle in the aorta. It travels to the capillaries of the tissues, where it releases oxygen and glucose for respiration and receives carbon dioxide and water. It travels back to the heart in the vena cava. It enters the right atrium and is pumped to the right ventricle. It leaves the heart in the pulmonary artery. It travels to the lungs to receive more oxygen and release carbon dioxide and water. It travels back to the heart in the pulmonary vein. It enters the left atrium and is pumped to the left ventricle.

(c) Arteries: Thick muscular walls to withstand high pressure **(1 mark)**; Veins: One-way valves to stop blood flowing backwards **(1 mark)**; Capillaries: Walls one cell thick to maximise diffusion into and from adjacent cells **(1 mark)**

(d) Oxygen and glucose **(1 mark)**; diffuse from the blood into the cells **(1 mark)**; Carbon dioxide and water **(1 mark)**; diffuse back from the cells to the blood **(1 mark)**

16. **(a)** **1 mark for name, 1 for function, e.g.** Mouth to begin breakdown of food; Stomach with acid to kill bacteria and enzymes to digest food; Liver to produce bile to help digest fat and neutralise acid; Pancreas to produce enzymes to digest food; Small intestine to absorb small soluble molecules; Large intestine to absorb water; Anus to release undigested material

(b) The rhythmic contraction and relaxation of the muscle wall in the oesophagus and small intestine to propel food forwards

(c) Carbohydrase; Lipase; Protease

17. **(a)** Identified the sequence of DNA bases of the human genome

(b) **Any two suitable examples, e.g.** To replace 'faulty' alleles for people who have genetic disorders; To compare DNA samples from potential crime suspects

(c) The information might be misused

18.* A diploid nucleus is taken from a body cell of the parent. An egg cell is enucleated (the chromosomes are removed). The diploid nucleus is inserted into the empty egg cell. This is called nuclear transfer. The egg cell is stimulated to begin cell division. The egg is implanted in the uterus of a surrogate mother. The embryo develops and is born as normal.

19. DNA unravels at the correct gene **(1 mark)**; A messenger RNA copy of the gene is made **(1 mark)**; This copy exits the nucleus and attaches to a ribosome in the cytoplasm **(1 mark)**; A transfer RNA copy of the messenger RNA is made **(1 mark)**; Transfer RNA brings amino acids, which are joined together to make a polypeptide (protein) **(1 mark)**

20. Pattern of limb bones found in all classes of tetrapods (vertebrates with four legs) **(1 mark)**; Many animals have evolved slightly different arrangements **(1 mark)**; Similarity of the bones in tetrapods indicates they have evolved from a single ancestor **(1 mark)**

Answers

21. (a) Covered with millions of small finger-like projections called villi **(1 mark)**; They provide a large surface area for maximum absorption **(1 mark)**; have a rich blood supply for maximum absorption **(1 mark)**; have walls one cell thick for maximum absorption **(1 mark)**

(b) (i) In the liver **(ii)** It neutralises stomach acid **(1 mark)**; and emulsifies fat **(1 mark)**

Unit C2

1. (a) Giant crystalline (or metallic) structure

(b) Sea of free electrons

(c) **Any three points, e.g.** Good conductor of heat; Good conductor of electricity; Have high melting and boiling points; Shiny, hard and strong; Ductile; Malleable

2. (a) Theoretical yield is calculated from relative formula masses of reactants and products **(1 mark)**; Actual yield is the actual mass of useful product obtained from a given amount of reactant in the experiment **(1 mark)**

(b) **Any suitable answer, e.g.** More economical; Cheaper process; Greater atom economy

(c) (i) $(\frac{31.5}{32.4}) \times 100 = 97.2\%$

(ii) RFM of ZnO = 65 + 16 = 81 **(1 mark)**; Percentage Zn in ZnO = $(\frac{65}{81}) \times 100 = 80.2\%$ **(1 mark)**

(iii) Mass of Zn = $(\frac{80.2}{100}) \times 31.5 = 25.3g$

3. (a) **Any suitable answer, e.g.** Because it gives out heat energy; The temperature of the reactants or surroundings increases/rises.

(b) Energy is needed to break the bonds in the reactants **(1 mark)**; Energy is given out when bonds are made in the products **(1 mark)**; In an exothermic reaction more energy is released in making bonds in the products than is needed to break bonds in the reactants **(1 mark)**

(c) Iodine **(1 mark)**; because chlorine is higher up the group / is more reactive **(1 mark)**

4. Helium is inert / doesn't react / is less dense than air so will float **(1 mark)**

5.* Iodine has a single covalent bond with one shared electron pair, and exists as a diatomic molecule. Because there are two atoms of iodine in each molecule it has a simple molecular structure. At room temperature iodine is a solid but it has a very low melting point because the intermolecular forces holding the diatomic molecules within their structure are weak. Weak intermolecular forces do not require much energy to overcome. This is why the melting points and boiling points of molecules with this type of structure are low – many are gases at room temperature. Iodine is unable to conduct electricity because a covalent bond does not involve the transfer of electrons or charged ions.

6. (a) Proton number is the same as the atomic number

(b) (1 mark each); Mg = 12, N = 7, S = 16

(c) Mass number – atomic number = number of neutrons

(d) (1 mark each)

7. (a) **Any three from:** Catalyst; Temperature; Concentration; Surface area; Pressure (in gases)

(b) Increases the rate of reaction

(c) There are fewer particles and they are spread out **(1 mark)** so there will be less chance of collisions **(1 mark)**

(d) Compare the same mass of calcium carbonate chips to finely crushed calcium carbonate in the reaction with hydrochloric acid **(1 mark)**; The volume of carbon dioxide produced is measured every minute **(1 mark)**; The same volume of carbon dioxide produced will be reached faster with the finely crushed calcium carbonate **(1 mark)**; Finely crushed calcium carbonate has a larger surface area so increases the rate of reaction **(1 mark)**

(e) Reduces the minimum amount of energy **(1 mark)** needed for the reaction to happen **(1 mark)**; This means that there will be more successful collisions between the particles **(1 mark)**

8. (a) C

(b) C

(c) (i) $BaCl_2$ (ii) MgO (iii) $AlCl_3$ (iv) Fe_2O_3

9. (a) $Mg(s) + Cl_2(g) \longrightarrow MgCl_2(s)$ **(2 marks)**

(b) $4Fe(s) + 3O_2(g) \longrightarrow 2Fe_2O_3(s)$ **(2 marks)**

10. (a) (i) Fe_2O_3: $(56 \times 2) + (16 \times 3) = 160$

(ii) Al_2O_3: $(2 \times 27) + (3 \times 16) = 102$

(b) (i) 800g $Fe_2O_3 = \frac{800}{160} = 5$ formula masses **(1 mark)**; From equation, each Fe_2O_3 reacts with 2 Al, so need $2 \times 5 = 10$ Al **(1 mark)**; Mass of Al $= 10 \times 27 = 270$g **(1 mark)**

(ii) 480g $Fe_2O_3 = \frac{480}{160} = 3$ formula masses **(1 mark)**; From equation, each Fe_2O_3 produces 2 Fe, so 3 formula masses of Fe_2O_3 produces $2 \times 3 = 6$ Fe **(1 mark)**; Mass of Fe $= 6 \times 56 = 336$g **(1 mark)**

(iii) 612g $Al_2O_3 = \frac{612}{102} = 6$ formula masses **(1 mark)**;

From equation, 2 Al is needed for each Al_2O_3, so need $2 \times 6 = 12$ Al **(1 mark)**; Mass of Al $= 12 \times 27 = 324$g **(1 mark)**

11. (a) Diamond has a giant molecular structure **(1 mark)**; Each of the carbon atoms forms four covalent bonds with other carbon atoms, making it a very hard substance **(1 mark)**; It has a very high melting point and boiling point but it is unable to conduct electricity because there are no available electrons **(1 mark)**

(b) In graphite the carbon atoms are only covalently bonded to three further carbon atoms, leaving the fourth electron from each atom to move freely about the structure **(1 mark)**; This allows graphite to conduct electricity **(1 mark)**; The atoms within the structure of graphite are arranged in layers that are able to slide past each other. This allows graphite to be used in pencils and as a lubricant **(1 mark)**

Unit P2

1. D

2. Any one from: Lightning; Sparks from synthetic clothing; Shocks from car doors; Charged balloon stuck to wall; Charged comb picking up bits of paper, etc.

3. Safe path for discharge / equalising imbalance of electrons

4. Voltmeter **(1 mark)** across / in parallel with a component **(1 mark)**

5. Fixed resistor: resistance constant **(1 mark)**; Thermistor: resistance decreases **(1 mark)** as temperature increases **(1 mark)**

6. P.d. $= I \times R = 1.5 \times 10 = 15$V

7. $a = \frac{(28 - 20)}{4}$ **(1 mark)** $= 2.0$m/s^2 **(1 mark)**

8. (a) $850 \times 2.0 = 1700$N

(b) Driving force – Resultant force = 2500N – 1700N **(1 mark)**; Resistive forces = 800N **(1 mark)**

9. Resultant force on parachutist is zero **(1 mark)**; Falling speed is constant **(1 mark)**

10. (a) Thinking distance and braking distance **(Both needed)**

(b) Any two from: Speed; Mass of vehicle; Condition of vehicle; Condition of the road; Driver's reaction time

11. (a) 24 000kg m/s **(b)** 36 000kg m/s

(c) 36 000kg m/s

12. They absorb (kinetic) energy **(1 mark)**; so time to stop is increased **(1 mark)**; reducing the force on the passengers **(1 mark)**

Answers

13. (a) Atom/element with same atomic number/proton number **(1 mark)** but different mass/nucleon number **(1 mark)**
(b) 8 **(c)** 9

14. (a) Gamma **(b)** Alpha **(c)** Alpha/β+ (positron)

15. (a) Radiation that occurs all around us
(b) **Any one from:** Radon; From medical use; Nuclear industry; Cosmic rays; Food

16. $\frac{1500}{375}$ = 4, so 2 half-lives **(1 mark)**; 2 half-lives = 2 × 3.5 hours = 7 hours **(1 mark)**; Time = 4pm **(1 mark)**

17.* It could be a good idea because a nuclear power station doesn't emit greenhouse gases, e.g carbon dioxide, or air pollutants (unlike fossil fuel power stations). Also many local jobs would be created. However, it costs a lot to build and run a nuclear power station. It produces dangerous waste and there is the risk of an accident (such as at Chernobyl or in Japan). Wildlife habitats could be destroyed or affected. In addition it would spoil the look of the countryside and it would create more traffic and noise in the area.

18. Fuel gains electrons from fuel pipe **(1 mark)**; Pipe becomes +ve and fuel becomes –ve **(1 mark)**; P.d. can cause spark/discharge **(1 mark)**; Prevent by earthing fuel tank/link tanker and plane with copper strip **(1 mark)**

19. Filament lamp: The curve shows the resistance increasing as the potential difference increases due to the filament getting hotter **(1 mark)**; When the current reaches a steady value the resistance remains constant **(1 mark)**
Diode: For the potential difference in one direction, the graph has a constant slope so the resistance is constant **(1 mark)**; For the potential difference in the opposite direction there is no current flowing so the resistance is infinitely high **(1 mark)**

20. (a) Energy transferred **(1 mark)** per unit charge passed **(1 mark)**
(b) P.d. = $\frac{E}{q}$ (E = energy, q = charge) **(1 mark)**; Units: p.d., V; E, J; q, C **(1 mark)**

21.* An electric current is the rate of flow of charge. In a metal this is a flow of electrons. Electrons have a negative charge. The greater the flow of electrons, the greater the flow of charge. When electrons move through the wire, some electrons collide with the ions of the metal lattice that the wire is made from. Each collision loses some energy to the wire as heat. This is because there is a transfer of the kinetic energy of the electrons to thermal energy of the ions. When a large current flows there are more collisions and this causes the wire to get hot.

22. Drag/air resistance increases upon opening the parachute, now greater than weight **(1 mark)**; Speed decreases so drag decreases **(1 mark)**; Until equal to weight **(1 mark)**

23. (a) Initial momentum = 0.12 × 4 = 0.48kg m/s **(1 mark)**; Final momentum = −0.12 × 3 = −0.36kg m/s **(1 mark)**; Change in momentum = 0.48 + 0.36 = 0.84kg m/s **(1 mark)**
(b) $\frac{0.84}{0.2}$ **(1 mark)** = 4.2N **(1 mark)**

24. $F \times d = \frac{1}{2}mv^2$ so $v^2 = \frac{2 \times F \times d}{m}$ **(1 mark)** = 2 × 2 000 × $\frac{50}{1200}$ **(1 mark)**; so $v = \sqrt{\frac{500}{3}}$ **(1 mark)** = 12.9m/s **(1 mark)**

25.* Nuclear fusion involves the joining together of two or more atomic nuclei to form a larger atomic nucleus. The problem in nuclear fusion is that both the nuclei have positive charges, so the nuclei repel each other. To bring the two nuclei close enough to be fused, the electrostatic force of repulsion needs to be overcome. This is possible by accelerating these nuclei to very high speeds. This acceleration is attained by heating the nuclei to very high temperatures. Extremely high pressures are also needed to force the nuclei into a very small space.

26. Not true **(1 mark)**; If source is outside: beta and gamma dangerous **(1 mark)**; they can penetrate but alpha can't **(1 mark)**; If source is inside: alpha is strongly ionising so alpha is dangerous as it is strongly absorbed **(1 mark)** but beta and gamma cause less interaction / absorption **(1 mark)**

Glossary

Acceleration – the rate of change of velocity of a body.

Aerobic – with oxygen. Aerobic respiration uses oxygen to release energy from organic molecules (food) and produce carbon dioxide and water.

Alkali metal – an element found in Group 1 of the periodic table. Atoms of these elements all contain a single electron in the outer energy level.

Alpha particles – consist of two protons and two neutrons (a helium nucleus); emitted from the nuclei of radioactive substances during alpha decay.

Amino acid – a building block of a protein. Amino acids link up to form proteins.

Amperes / amps (A) – the unit used to measure electric current.

Anaerobic – without oxygen. Anaerobic respiration occurs when not enough oxygen is present and is the incomplete breakdown of glucose to release a small amount of energy and produce lactic acid.

Asexual reproduction – a form of reproduction that does not involve fertilisation. The offspring are clones (i.e. genetically identical to the parent).

Atom – smallest particle of a chemical element that can exist.

Atomic (proton) number (Z) – the number of protons in the nucleus of an atom.

Background radiation – radiation from the environment.

Becquerel (Bq) – the unit of radioactivity; one nuclear disintegration per second.

Beta particles – fast-moving electrons (β –) or positrons (β +); emitted from the nuclei of radioactive substances during beta electrons decay.

Biodiversity – the variety of different types of organisms in a habitat or ecosystem.

Braking distance – distance travelled by a vehicle while braking.

Catalyst – a substance that is used to speed up a chemical reaction without itself being used. At the end of the reaction, a catalyst will not be chemically changed.

Cell membrane – surrounds cells and controls the movement of chemicals and particles into and out of the cell.

Cellulose cell wall – a carbohydrate that forms walls in plant cells. It provides the cells with structural support.

Chain reaction – a self-sustaining series of reactions, such as nuclear fission, in which the neutrons released in one fission trigger the fission of other nuclei.

Chemical reaction – a process that leads to the transformation of one set of chemical substances to another.

Chloride ions – chlorine atoms that have gained an additional electron as a result of chemical reaction.

Chloroplast – a component found in the green parts of plants; contains chlorophyll for photosynthesis.

Chromatography – a technique used to separate unknown mixtures for analysis.

Chromosome – made up of DNA and protein; consists of a series of genes.

Clone – an individual that is genetically identical to its parent.

Compound – a substance that contains two or more different atoms of one or more elements chemically combined.

Compound ion – a positively or negatively charged particle formed when a group of atoms lose or gain electrons.

Conservation of energy – a law that states that energy cannot be made or lost: it can only be transferred from one form into another.

Control rods – devices used to control the power of a nuclear reactor.

Glossary

Covalent bond – the sharing of electron pairs between non-metals.

Crumple zone – the part of a vehicle's structure designed to collapse or crumple in a collision and so reduce the force on passengers.

Current – the rate of flow of electrons through a conductor (measured in amperes / amps (A), milliamps (mA)).

Cytoplasm – everything inside a cell that is not the nucleus or another component. It is mostly water and usually clear in colour.

Daughter nucleus – a nucleus produced by radioactive decay of another nucleus (the parent).

Differentiation – the process by which a cell becomes specialised to perform a specific function.

Diffusion – the movement of particles from an area of high concentration to an area of lower concentration down a concentration gradient.

Diode – an electronic component that allows current to flow in one direction only.

DNA – the substance from which chromosomes are made.

Earthing – enables electrons to flow from one object to earth to allow discharge.

Electronic configuration – the orbital/shell arrangement of electrons around the nucleus of an atom.

Elongation – the lengthening of plant cells caused by the hormones auxin and gibberellin.

Empirical formula – the simplest formula of a compound.

Enzyme – a protein molecule and biological catalyst, found in living organisms, which helps chemical reactions to take place.

Fission – the splitting of large atomic nuclei that produces a large amount of energy.

Fractional distillation – a method of separating a mixture of liquids that have different boiling points.

Fusion – the joining together of small atomic nuclei, producing a large amount of energy.

Gametes – sex cells (i.e. sperm and eggs)

Gamma rays – high-frequency electromagnetic waves with a short wavelength.

Gene – the part of a chromosome that controls the development of a particular characteristic.

Genetic engineering – the technology that involves moving genes (DNA) from one organism to another. It can be within species or between species.

Gravitational potential energy (GPE) – one form of potential energy: the product of the weight of an object and its change in altitude; measured in joules (J).

Half-life – the time taken for half of the undecayed nuclei in radioactive material to decay.

Halide – compound formed from the chemical reaction of a halogen.

Halogens – non-metals found in Group 7 of the periodic table. Known as the 'salt-formers', they exist as diatomic molecules.

Insoluble – a substance that will not dissolve in a solvent and is unable to form a solution.

Ion – a positively or negatively charged particle formed when an atom or group of atoms lose or gain electrons.

Ionic bond – a chemical bond in which one atom loses an electron to form a positive ion and the other atom gains an electron to form a negative ion.

Ionisation – an atom losing (or gaining) electrons as a result of energy gained by interaction with a particle or radiation.

Ionising radiation – a stream of high-energy particles / rays: alpha, beta, gamma; can damage human cells and tissues.

Isotopes – atoms of the same element that have the same number of protons but a different number of neutrons.

Glossary

Kinetic energy (KE) – the energy possessed by a moving object; measured in joules (J).

Light-dependent resistor (LDR) – an electronic component the resistance of which varies with light intensity.

Mass – a measure of how much matter an object contains.

Mass (nucleon) number (A) – the total number of protons and neutrons (nucleons) in the nucleus of an atom.

Meiosis – a type of division in a cell's nucleus that produces sex cells (gametes).

Mendeleev, Dmitri – Russian chemist who devised the arrangement of the modern periodic table.

Metal atom – an atom of an element on the left-hand side of the periodic table.

Metal compound – a substance that contains atoms of one or more elements chemically combined, one of which will be a metal.

Metal ions – formed when metal atoms lose electrons.

Metal oxides – formed when a metal ion combines with an oxide ion.

Mitochondria – a component found in most plant and animal cells, which is the major site of respiration.

Mitosis – a type of division in a cell's nucleus that produces new diploid cells for growth, or to replace damaged cells.

Moderator – substance used to slow down fast neutrons and to increase the power of a nuclear reactor.

Momentum – a measure of the state of motion of an object; given by mass × velocity (a vector quantity); measured in kg m/s.

Mutation – a change in the genetic material of a cell (or virus).

Neutron – uncharged particle found in the nucleus of almost all atoms.

Noble gases – unreactive non-metallic elements found in Group 0 of the periodic table.

Nuclear reactor – a device in which a nuclear fission chain reaction is controlled to produce energy in the form of electricity.

Nucleus – the part of a cell that contains chromosomes.

Ohm (Ω) – the unit of electrical resistance; 1 ohm is the resistance of a conducting material across which a potential difference of 1V causes a current of 1A to flow.

Osmosis – the net movement of water particles from a high to a low concentration of water across a partially permeable membrane.

Period – a horizontal row of elements with a variety of properties and the same number of electron shells.

Periodic table – a tabular display of all known discovered elements.

Peristalsis – rhythmic waves of muscle contraction and relaxation that move food along the oesophagus and small intestine.

Phloem – tissue that conducts nutrients around plants.

Photosynthesis – the process by which green plants use light energy to make glucose.

Potential difference (p.d.) – same as voltage: difference in electrical voltage between two points in a circuit; expressed in volts (V).

Power – the rate at which work is done or energy is transferred by a device; measured in watts, 1W = 1J/s; also refers to the strength of a lens, measured in dioptres, D.

Prebiotics – non-digestible foods that stimulate the growth of bacteria in the digestive system.

Precipitate – the name given to the solid that is formed as a result of a precipitation reaction.

Precipitation reaction – the formation of an insoluble solid when two solutions are mixed.

Probiotics – foods that contain live microorganisms, commonly Lactobacillus and Bifidobacterium.

Protein – a food group; proteins are made up of long chains of amino acids.

Proton – a positively charged particle found in the nucleus of every atom.

Quadrat – a square frame that is placed on the ground during sampling to count the number or type of organisms within it.

Radiation – the process of transferring energy by electromagnetic waves; also particles e.g. alpha, beta emitted by a radioactive substance.

Radioactive – materials containing unstable nuclei that spontaneously decay.

Radioactive decay – the emission of particles from an unstable nucleus.

Radiotherapy – the use of ionising radiation in the treatment of cancer.

Relative atomic mass – the average mass of an atom compared with the mass of an atom of carbon.

Relative formula mass – the sum of the relative atomic masses as shown in a chemical formula.

Resistance – the property of materials to resist the flow of electric current through them or a force that opposes motion.

Respiration – the process by which energy is released from glucose.

Resultant force – the total force acting on an object (all the forces combined).

Sampling – investigating a smaller section of a habitat to draw conclusions about the whole. Sampling techniques include transects, sweep netting and kick sampling.

Sexual reproduction – a form of reproduction that involves the fusion of an egg with a sperm during fertilisation, which results in genetic variation.

Soluble – a substance that will dissolve in a solvent to form a solution.

Stem cell – an undifferentiated cell that has the potential to develop into a specialised cell.

Stopping distance – how long it takes a vehicle to stop; the sum of the thinking distance and the braking distance.

Terminal velocity – the constant velocity reached by a falling body when the resultant force is zero.

Thermistor – an electronic component of the resistance of which varies with temperature.

Thinking distance – the distance travelled by a vehicle during the reaction time.

Transition metals – found in the middle of the periodic table.

Transpiration – the loss of water from plants, especially from their leaves.

Tumour – a group of cells that divide without control imposed by the body; they may be malignant (severe or fatal) or benign (mild).

Vacuole – a large space in the centre of a plant cell, which is full of cell sap.

Variation – the differences between organisms of the same species.

Vector – an organism (often a microorganism) used to transfer a gene, or genes, from one organism to another; also used to describe an organism that transmits a disease, e.g. the mosquito is a vector of the malarial parasite.

Velocity – the speed at which an object moves in a particular direction.

Velocity–time graph – velocity against time taken; the gradient gives the acceleration; the area under the graph gives the distance travelled.

Volt (V) – the unit of potential difference or voltage.

Voltage – the value of the potential difference between two points, such as the terminals of a cell.

Weight – the gravitational force acting on a body.

Glossary

White blood cell – part of the body's immune system; they either engulf bacteria (phagocytes) or produce antibodies (lymphocytes).

Work – the energy transfer that occurs when a force causes an object to move a certain distance.

Work done – the product of the force applied to a body and the distance moved in the direction of the force; measured in joules (J).

X-rays – a region of the electromagnetic spectrum between gamma rays and ultraviolet rays; X-rays can be emitted when a solid target is bombarded with electrons.

Xylem – tissue that transports water and mineral ions in a plant from the roots to the shoots.

(HT) **Genome** – all the genetic material of an organism.

Human Genome Project – an international project that set out to establish the sequence of all the bases in the genes of all 23 pairs of human chromosomes.

Key

relative atomic mass
atomic symbol
name
atomic (proton) number

1	hydrogen	1

1	2												3	4	5	6	7	0
																		4 **He** helium 2
7 **Li** lithium 3	9 **Be** beryllium 4												11 **B** boron 5	12 **C** carbon 6	14 **N** nitrogen 7	16 **O** oxygen 8	19 **F** fluorine 9	20 **Ne** neon 10
23 **Na** sodium 11	24 **Mg** magnesium 12												27 **Al** aluminium 13	28 **Si** silicon 14	31 **P** phosphorus 15	32 **S** sulfur 16	35.5 **Cl** chlorine 17	40 **Ar** argon 18
39 **K** potassium 19	40 **Ca** calcium 20	45 **Sc** scandium 21	48 **Ti** titanium 22	51 **V** vanadium 23	52 **Cr** chromium 24	55 **Mn** manganese 25	56 **Fe** iron 26	59 **Co** cobalt 27	59 **Ni** nickel 28	63.5 **Cu** copper 29	65 **Zn** zinc 30	70 **Ga** gallium 31	73 **Ge** germanium 32	75 **As** arsenic 33	79 **Se** selenium 34	80 **Br** bromine 35	84 **Kr** krypton 36
85 **Rb** rubidium 37	88 **Sr** strontium 38	89 **Y** yttrium 39	91 **Zr** zirconium 40	93 **Nb** niobium 41	96 **Mo** molybdenum 42	[98] **Tc** technetium 43	101 **Ru** ruthenium 44	103 **Rh** rhodium 45	106 **Pd** palladium 46	108 **Ag** silver 47	112 **Cd** cadmium 48	115 **In** indium 49	119 **Sn** tin 50	122 **Sb** antimony 51	128 **Te** tellurium 52	127 **I** iodine 53	131 **Xe** xenon 54
133 **Cs** caesium 55	137 **Ba** barium 56	139 **La*** lanthanum 57	178 **Hf** hafnium 72	181 **Ta** tantalum 73	184 **W** tungsten 74	186 **Re** rhenium 75	190 **Os** osmium 76	192 **Ir** iridium 77	195 **Pt** platinum 78	197 **Au** gold 79	201 **Hg** mercury 80	204 **Tl** thallium 81	207 **Pb** lead 82	209 **Bi** bismuth 83	[209] **Po** polonium 84	[210] **At** astatine 85	[222] **Rn** radon 86
[223] **Fr** francium 87	[226] **Ra** radium 88	[227] **Ac*** actinium 89	[261] **Rf** rutherfordium 104	[262] **Db** dubnium 105	[266] **Sg** seaborgium 106	[264] **Bh** bohrium 107	[277] **Hs** hassium 108	[268] **Mt** meitnerium 109	[271] **Ds** darmstadtium 110	[272] **Rg** roentgenium 111							

Elements with atomic numbers 112–116 have been reported but not fully authenticated

*The lanthanoids (atomic numbers 58–71) and the actinoids (atomic numbers 90–103) have been omitted.

The relative atomic masses of copper and chlorine have not been rounded to the nearest whole number.

Index

Two elements in group 1

Describe the similarities & differences in what is seen on in the products of the reactions

test gas produce CO_2